IMPACT

CALIFORNIA SOCIAL STUDIES

A Child's Place
In Time and Space

INQUIRY JOURNAL

McGraw Hill

Program Authors

James Banks, Ph.D.
Kerry and Linda Killinger Endowed Chair
in Diversity Studies
Director, Center for Multicultural Education
University of Washington
Seattle, Washington

Kevin P. Colleary, Ed.D.
Curriculum and Teaching Department
Graduate School of Education
Fordham University
New York, New York

William Deverell, Ph.D.
Director of the Huntington-USC Institute
on California and the West
Professor of History, University
of Southern California
Los Angeles, California

Daniel Lewis, Ph.D.
Dibner Senior Curator
The Huntington Library
Los Angeles, California

Elizabeth Logan Ph.D., J.D.
Associate Director of the Huntington-
USC Institute on California and the West
Los Angeles, California

Walter C. Parker, Ph.D.
Professor of Social Studies Education
Adjunct Professor of Political Science
University of Washington
Seattle, Washington

Emily M. Schell, Ed.D.
Professor, Teacher Education
San Diego State University
San Diego, California

mheducation.com/prek-12

Send all inquiries to:
McGraw-Hill Education
120 S. Riverside Plaza, Suite 1200
Chicago, IL 60606

ISBN: 978-0-07-899395-4
MHID: 0-07-899395-4

Printed in the United States of America.

7 8 9 10 11 12 13 WEB 25 24 23 22 21

Program Consultants

Jana Echevarria, Ph.D.
Professor Emerita
California State University
Long Beach, California

Douglas Fisher, Ph.D.
Professor, Educational Leadership
San Diego State University
San Diego, California

Carlos Ulloa, Ed.D.
Principal, Escondido Union School District
Escondido, California

Rebecca Valbuena, M.Ed.
K-5 Teacher on Special Assignment/Academic Coach
Glendora Unified School District
Glendora, California

Program Reviewers

Gary Clayton, Ph.D.
Professor of Economics
Northern Kentucky University
Highland Heights, Kentucky

Lorri Glover, Ph.D.
John Francis Bannon, S.J. Professor of History
Saint Louis University
St. Louis, Missouri

Thomas Herman, Ph.D.
Project Director, Center for Interdisciplinary
Studies of Youth and Space
Department of Geography
San Diego State University

Nafees Khan, Ph.D.
Department of Teaching and Learning
Social Studies Education
Clemson University
Clemson, South Carolina

Clifford Trafzer, Ph.D.
Distinguished Professor of History
Rupert Costo Chair in American Indian Affairs
University of California
Riverside, California

Letter from the Authors

Dear Social Studies Detective,

Think about the world around you. Where do you live? What makes your community and the people who live in it special? What makes you special? In this book, you will find out how many different people make one big nation!

As you read, be an investigator. What do you wonder about? Write your questions. Then look for the answers while you read. What interests and excites you? Take notes about it. Then use your notes to do a project. Share what you learned! Take a closer look at photos of real people and places. Use maps to find your way!

Enjoy your investigation into the amazing world of social studies—a world where each person is special, and each person has a place!

Sincerely,
The IMPACT Social Studies Authors

Japanese American children in school in the 1940s

Contents

Reference Sources

Being a Good Citizen

What Are the Rights and Responsibilities of Citizens?

Chapter 2

Our Community

How Can We Describe Where We Live?

Chapter 3

Celebrating America

 How Do We Celebrate Our Country?

Chapter 4

Past and Present

How Is Our Life Different from the Past, and How Is It the Same?

Chapter 5

People of America

 How Do Many Different People Make One Nation?

Chapter

6

People and Money

Why Do People Work?

Skills and Features

My Notes

_____

_____

_____

_____

_____

_____

_____

_____

_____

_____

Getting Started

You have two social studies books that you will use together to explore and analyze important Social Studies issues.

The Inquiry Journal

The Inquiry Journal is your reporter's notebook where you will ask questions, analyze sources, and record information.

The Research Companion

The Research Companion is where you'll read nonfiction and literature selections, examine primary source materials, and look for answers to your questions.

Every Chapter

Chapter opener pages help you see the big picture. Each chapter begins with an **Essential Question**. This **EQ** guides research and inquiry.

In the **Research Companion**, you'll explore the EQ through words and photographs.

In the **Inquiry Journal**, you'll talk about the EQ and find out about the EQ Inquiry Project for the chapter.

Explore Words

Find out what you know about the chapter's academic vocabulary.

Connect Through Literature

Explore the chapter topic through fiction, informational text, and poetry.

Connect Through Literature

Pass It On
By Sara Matson
Art by John Joven

One summer day, Mouse packed a picnic. *I'll walk to the pond,* she thought. *I'll sit on the soft grass. I'll watch dragonflies sparkling in the sun.*

She was almost there when she heard a croak: "Help!"

Mouse followed the sound to the pond. Frog was there, tugging on something. "What's wrong, Frog?" Mouse asked.

"My foot is stuck in this fishnet," Frog cried.

Mouse went over to help. She nibbled the net strings with her sharp teeth. By the time Mouse got Frog unstuck, it was too late for her picnic.

Frog hopped high in the air. "How can I thank you, Mouse?"

"No need," Mouse said. "Just pass it on."

So Frog did.

4   Chapter 1   Being a Good Citizen

The next day, Frog played lily-pad leap in the pond. He heard a sneeze: *"Achoo!"*

Frog followed the sound to the meadow. Skunk was there, wiping her nose.

"What's wrong, Skunk?" Frog asked.

"I have a cold," Skunk said.

Frog helped Skunk home. He tucked her into bed. He poured her a cup of clover tea. He read her a story.

Skunk yawned. "How can I thank you, Frog?"

"No need," Frog said. "Just pass it on."

So Skunk did.

How can I thank you?

Chapter 1   5

People You Should Know

Learn about the lives of people who have made an impact in history.

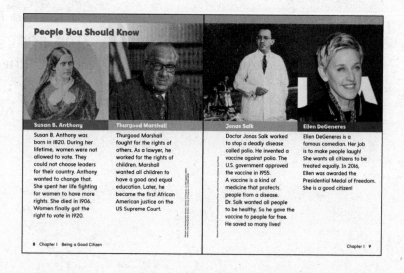

People You Should Know

Susan B. Anthony
Susan B. Anthony was born in 1820. During her lifetime, women were not allowed to vote. They could not choose leaders for their country. Anthony wanted to change that. She spent her life fighting for women to have more rights. She died in 1906. Women finally got the right to vote in 1920.

Thurgood Marshall
Thurgood Marshall fought for the rights of others. As a lawyer, he worked for the rights of children. Marshall wanted all children to have a good and equal education. Later, he became the first African American justice on the US Supreme Court.

Jonas Salk
Doctor Jonas Salk worked to stop a deadly disease called polio. He invented a vaccine against polio. The U.S. government approved the vaccine in 1955. A vaccine is a kind of medicine that protects people from a disease. Dr. Salk wanted all people to be healthy. So he gave the vaccine to people for free. He saved so many lives!

Ellen DeGeneres
Ellen DeGeneres is a famous comedian. Her job is to make people laugh! She wants all citizens to be treated equally. In 2016, Ellen was awarded the Presidential Medal of Freedom. She is a good citizen!

8   Chapter 1   Being a Good Citizen

Chapter 1   9

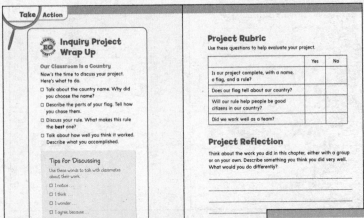

Take Action

Present your Inquiry Project to your class and assess your work with the project rubric. Then take time to think about your work.

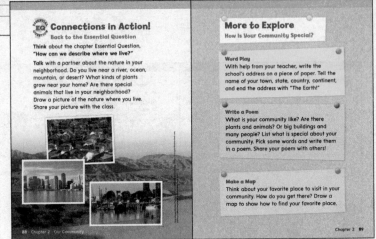

Connections in Action

Think about the people, places, and events you read about in the chapter. Does this change how you think about the EQ? Talk with a partner about it.

Every Lesson

Lesson Question lets you think about how the lesson connects to the chapter EQ.

Lesson Outcomes help you think about what you will be learning and how it applies to the EQ.

Images and text provide opportunities to explore the lesson topic.

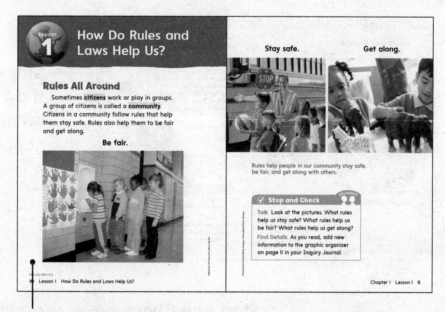

Lesson selections help you develop a deeper understanding of the lesson topic and the EQ.

Analyze and Inquire

The **Inquiry Journal** provides the tools you need to analyze a source. You'll use those tools to investigate the texts in the **Research Companion** and use the graphic organizer in the **Inquiry Journal** to organize your findings.

Inquiry Tools help you analyze and explore.

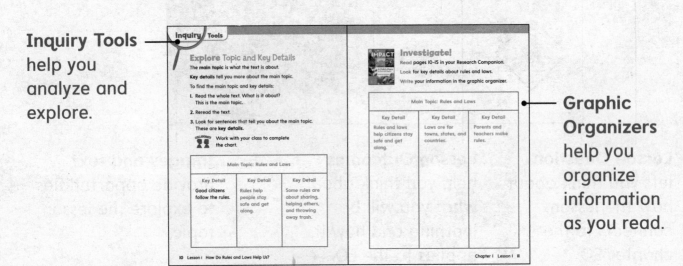

Graphic Organizers help you organize information as you read.

Primary Sources let you read the words and study the artifacts of people from the past and present.

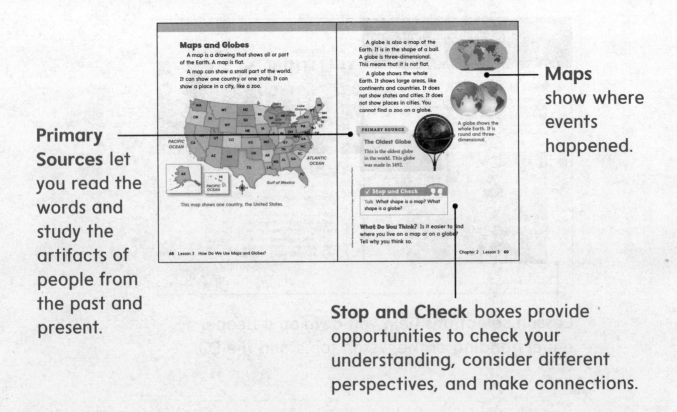

Maps show where events happened.

Stop and Check boxes provide opportunities to check your understanding, consider different perspectives, and make connections.

Report Your Findings

At the end of each lesson, you have an opportunity in the **Inquiry Journal** to report your findings and connect back to the EQ. In the Research Companion, you'll think about the lesson focus question.

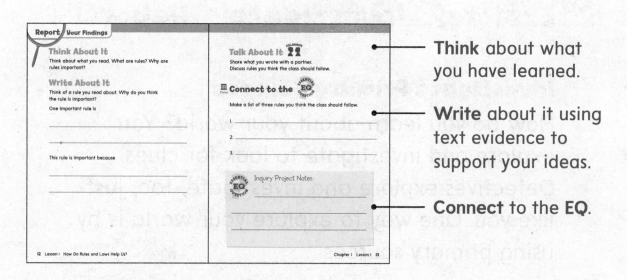

Think about what you have learned.

Write about it using text evidence to support your ideas.

Connect to the EQ.

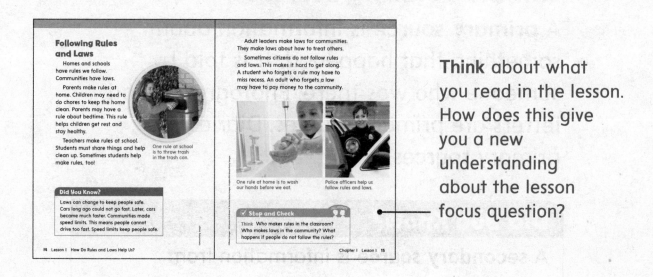

Think about what you read in the lesson. How does this give you a new understanding about the lesson focus question?

Be a Social Studies Detective

How do you learn about people, places, and events? Become a Social Studies Detective!

Explore!   Investigate!   Report!

Investigate Primary Sources

How do you learn about your world? You explore and investigate to look for clues. Detectives explore and investigate, too, just like you. One way to explore your world is by using primary sources

What Are Primary Sources?

A **primary source** is information about something that happened. It is told by someone who was there. Photographs and letters are primary sources. Diaries are primary sources, too.

Did You Know?

A **secondary source** is information from someone who was not present at the event he or she is describing. Secondary sources are based on primary sources, such as a newspaper article.

StasKhom/iStock/Getty Images

Look at the pictures. Ask questions.

Is it real?

Or is it make believe?

Is it a drawing?

Or is it a photo?

Talk About It

COLLABORATE

Look at the pictures. Which picture do you think is a primary source?

Boys playing in New York City, 1904

Look closely.

What else do you see?

Talk About It

Who is in the picture? What are they doing?
How do you know?

What are you looking at?

Is this picture from now or long ago?

Look closely.

Find details in the picture.

What clues do you see?

Talk About It

COLLABORATE

What are these children doing? What detail in the picture is your clue?

Explore Geography

Geographers are social studies detectives who study the Earth's surface, plants, animals, and people. They use tools to help them investigate. Here are a few of the tools you need to be a geographer.

Models, Maps, and Photos

Look at the model of the playground. A model is a small copy of a place or object.

Look at the photo of another playground. This photo shows a different playground. How is it different from the model?

Look at the map of the playground.
A map is a drawing of a place.

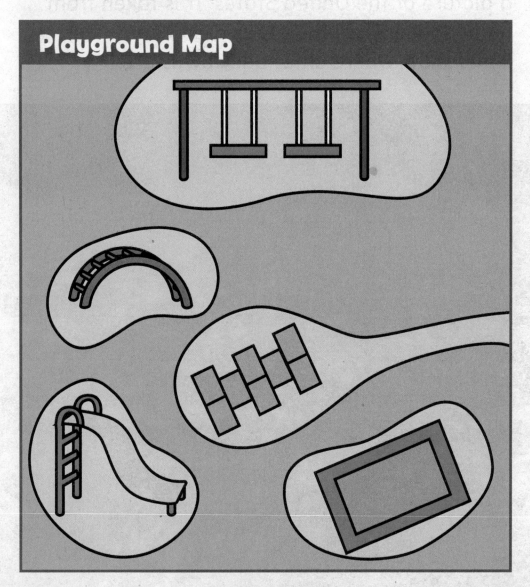

Playground Map

Talk About It

How are a model, map, and photo the same?
How are they different?

Picturing Earth

Earth is our home. It is round, like a ball. This is a picture of the United States. It is taken from outer space. The blue areas are oceans. The lights show where cities and towns are.

Anton Balazh/Shutterstock.com

This is a model of Earth. It is called a globe. It shows what the land and water look like on Earth. The equator is a line around the middle of the globe. It divides Earth into two equal parts: North and South.

Talk About It

COLLABORATE

What does the globe show? How are a globe and a map similar?

Explore Economics

Workers produce goods and services. A good is something you can touch like food, clothes, and toys. A service is something that one person does for another. The mechanic in the picture is fixing a car. That is a service.

Talk About It

What are some other examples of goods and services? What goods do you see in the picture below?

Explore Citizenship

You can make an impact by being a good citizen. The words on the next page describe good citizens. These words help us understand how to be good citizens in our home, neighborhood, school, community, country, and world.

Workers repair an American flag

Take Action!

You have learned to be a Social Studies Detective by investigating, finding evidence, and making connections. Then you practiced investigating geography, economics, and civics. Now it's time to explore and make an impact!

Be a Good Citizen

COURAGE
Being brave

FREEDOM
Making our
own choices

HONESTY
Telling the truth

JUSTICE
Being fair to everyone

LEADERSHIP
Showing good
behavior and being
a good example

LOYALTY
Showing support for
people and one's
country

RESPECT
Treating others as
you would like to
be treated

RESPONSIBILITY
Being someone
people can trust

Chapter 1

Being a Good Citizen

ESSENTIAL EQ QUESTION

What Are the Rights and Responsibilities of Citizens?

In this chapter, you'll explore the rights and responsibilities of a good citizen. You'll read about some things good citizens do. You'll also work on a team chapter project where you think about rights and responsibilities of citizens in a country you create!

Talk About It 👥 COLLABORATE

Discuss with a partner questions you have about rights and responsibilities of citizens.

My Research Questions

1._____

_____

2._____

_____

HSS 1.1, HSS 1.1.1, HSS 1.1.2, HSS 1.3.3, HSS 1.4.1, HSS 1.4.2, HSS 1.4.3, HAS.CS.1.1, HAS.CS.1.2, HAS.CS.1.3

Inquiry Project

Our Classroom Is a Country

In this project, you'll work with a team to imagine your classroom is a country. Name your country, draw a flag for your country, and come up with a rule the people of your country will follow.

Here's your project checklist.

☐ **Brainstorm** ideas for your country's name. Then vote on one idea.

☐ **Make** a new flag. Be sure it is colorful. It should tell something about your country.

☐ **List** some ideas for rules for your country. How will these rules help people be good citizens?

☐ **Choose** the best rule for your citizens.

☐ **Write** the rule so that it's big enough for everyone to read!

Explore Words

Complete this chapter's Word Rater. Write notes as you learn more about each word.

citizen   My Notes

☐ Know It!   _____
☐ Heard It!
☐ Don't Know It!   _____

community   My Notes

☐ Know It!   _____
☐ Heard It!
☐ Don't Know It!   _____

democracy   My Notes

☐ Know It!   _____
☐ Heard It!
☐ Don't Know It!   _____

law   My Notes

☐ Know It!   _____
☐ Heard It!
☐ Don't Know It!   _____

past   My Notes

☐ Know It!   _____
☐ Heard It!
☐ Don't Know It!   _____

respect

My Notes

- ☐ Know It!
- ☐ Heard It!
- ☐ Don't Know It!

_____

_____

responsibility

My Notes

- ☐ Know It!
- ☐ Heard It!
- ☐ Don't Know It!

_____

_____

rights

My Notes

- ☐ Know It!
- ☐ Heard It!
- ☐ Don't Know It!

_____

_____

voting

My Notes

- ☐ Know It!
- ☐ Heard It!
- ☐ Don't Know It!

_____

_____

How Do Rules and Laws Help Us?

Lesson Outcomes

What Am I Learning?
You will explore how rules and laws help us.

Why Am I Learning It?
You will learn how rules and laws help groups of people live together.

How Will I Know that I Learned It?
You will list rules and laws that help people stay safe and work together.

Talk About It

Look closely at the student. What is she doing? What rules is she following?

satit_srihin/Shutterstock.com

HSS 1.1.1

What Are Rules?

Read Look at the title. What do you think this text will be about?

Circle words you don't know.

Underline clues that tell you:

• Why do we have rules?
• Who follows rules?

My Notes

_____

_____

_____

_____

Rules tell us what to do. Rules help us stay safe. Rules help us get along.

One rule is to walk when you are inside. This rule keeps people safe. It is not safe to run inside.

Good citizens follow rules. **Citizens** are people in a group. Citizens work or play together.

Rules help us have fun. Rules help us get jobs done. It is good for citizens to follow rules.

Students raise their hands to talk in class. Students follow the rules.

©KidStock/Blend Images

Students are citizens of a classroom. Students follow class rules. One rule is to always put trash in the trash can. This rule keeps the room clean.

Students share computers and other tools. Sharing is an important rule. Sharing helps everyone get a turn.

The rules in your class help students learn and work together.

More people get to use classroom supplies when they are shared.

Hero Images/Image Source

2 Find Evidence

Reread Why do people follow rules?

Underline clues that tell why people follow rules.

3 Make Connections

Talk Turn back to page 7. COLLABORATE How are the people in this picture being good citizens? What rules are they following? Why are these rules important?

Explore Topic and Key Details

The **main topic** is what the text is about.

Key details tell you more about the main topic.

To find the main topic and key details:

1. Read the whole text. What is it about? This is the main topic.

2. Reread the text.

3. Look for sentences that tell you about the main topic. These are **key details.**

COLLABORATE Work with your class to complete the chart.

Main Topic: Rules and Laws		
Key Detail Good citizens follow the rules.	**Key Detail**	**Key Detail**

Investigate!

Read pages 10–15 in your Research Companion.

Look for key details about rules and laws.

Write your information in the graphic organizer.

Main Topic: Rules and Laws		
Key Detail	Key Detail	Key Detail

Think About It

Think about what you read. What are rules? Why are rules important?

Write About It

Think of a rule you read about. Why do you think the rule is important?

One important rule is

_____

_____

This rule is important because

_____

_____

Talk About It

Share what you wrote with a partner.
Discuss rules you think the class should follow.

🏛 Connect to the EQ
Civics

Make a list of three rules you think the class should follow.

1. _____

2. _____

3. _____

Inquiry Project Notes

_____

_____

_____

How Can We Get Along With Each Other?

Lesson Outcomes

What Am I Learning?

You will explore how people solve problems and reach fair decisions.

Why Am I Learning It?

You will see how people find ways to work together and get along.

How Will I Know that I Learned it?

You will suggest different ways for people to solve problems and agree with each other.

Talk About It

Look closely at the picture. What are they doing? Are they getting along well together? How do you know?

Read Look at the pictures. What do you think this selection will be about?

Circle words you don't know.

Underline clues that tell you:

- What makes people disagree?
- What happens when they disagree?

My Notes

_____

_____

_____

Good Citizens Get Along Together

People don't always have the same ideas. When people disagree, they talk about it. They share ideas. They find a way to do things that make everyone happy. They find ways to agree.

Children can help each other. They can share things like snacks. They can teach each other new skills, like how to skate or ride a bike. Children can help their classmates solve problems.

People share, and people help each other get along.

(l)Ariel Skelley/age fotostock; (tr)FamVeld/Shutterstock.com; (br)Image Source/Getty Images

The classroom is messy. It needs to be cleaned up. The desks must be cleared. The books need to be put on the shelves.

The teacher splits up the work. One group clears the desks. The other group puts books away. Everyone helps. When everyone helps, people get along.

Splitting up the work helps everyone get along.

2 Find Evidence

Reread What do the pictures show you about people getting along?

Draw a box around the words that tell how people get along.

3 Make Connections

Talk Look back at the text on page 16. What problems do the children have? How do they solve the problems?

Explore Problem and Solution

A **problem** is something that goes wrong and needs to be fixed.

A **solution** is the way a person solves or fixes the problem.

To find the problem and solution:

1. Read the whole text.

2. Look for something wrong that needs to be fixed. This is the problem. Circle it.

3. Underline the sentences that show how the problem is fixed. This is the solution.

4. Ask yourself, *Does the solution make sense? Does it fix the problem?*

 COLLABORATE   Work with your class to fill in the chart.

Problem	Solution
The classroom is very messy and needs to be cleaned up.	

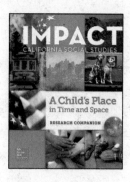

Investigate!

Read pages 16–23 in your Research Companion.

Look for details about problems and their solutions.

Write the details you find in the chart.

Problem	Solution
Two goats want to cross the bridge at the same time. There is not enough room.	
	Amy and Chamara compromise. Amy uses the calculator on the first problem. Chamara uses it on the second problem.

Think About It

Review your research. Think about the different ways people get along. Can you name two ways?

Write About It

What is one good way to get along with others? Use an example from what you read.

One way to get along is to _____

_____

_____

_____

An example of this is _____

_____

_____

_____

Talk About It

Explain

Share your response with a partner. Talk together about ways to get along in the classroom.

Citizenship

Connect to the EQ

Take Action

Read about the problems below. Work with a partner. Come up with a solution for each problem.

1. Three children want to color in red, but there is only one red crayon.

2. One of your classmates is angry or upset.

3. Some people in the class want a new classroom rule. Others don't want the rule.

Inquiry Project Notes

_____

_____

_____

_____

How Should Citizens Treat Each Other?

Lesson Outcomes

What Am I Learning?

You will explore how citizens should treat each other and how to be fair.

Why Am I Learning it?

You will know how a person can help others.

How Will I Know that I Learned it?

You will list things you could do to help others in your community.

Talk About It

Look closely at the picture. What are the boys doing? Would it be fun to play on their team? Why?

Games are more fun
when we help each other.

Read Look at the title. What do you think this text will be about?

Circle words you don't know.

Underline clues that tell you:

- What does respect mean?
- How do we show respect?
- What are you thinking about when you show respect?

My Notes

_____

_____

_____

Respect Everyone

How should people treat each other? We help each other. We take turns and share. We play fair. When we do this, we show **respect**. Respect means being polite. It means thinking about how another person feels. Respect is being kind. It is being fair.

These students are working together. They are being polite and showing each other respect.

shironosov/iStock/Getty Images

The students are showing respect for the land by cleaning up.

We respect people's **rights**. Rights are things that people deserve. Everyone has the right to be treated the same. People come from many places. They can be young or old. They can be big or small. They can be the same as others or different from others. We respect everyone's rights.

2 Find Evidence

Reread How does the text describe differences between people?

Underline the right that everyone has.

3 Make Connections

Talk Why are games more fun when we respect each other?

COLLABORATE

Look back at the picture on page 23. How are the students showing **respect** for each other?

Use Text and Visuals

Text is the group of words on a page.

Visuals are pictures, maps, and photos.

To use text and visuals:

1. Read the title. The title tells what the text is about.

2. Look at the visuals. How do they add to the text?

3. Read the caption. The caption is the sentence under the picture.

 COLLABORATE Based on the text and visuals, work with your class to complete the chart.

Page Number	What I Learn from the Text	What I Learn from the Visuals
24	It is important to respect people.	
25		

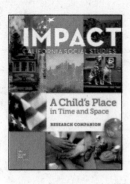

Investigate!

Read pages 24–29 in your Research Companion.

Look for clues from the text and visuals.

Write your notes in this chart.

Page Number	What I Learn from the Text	What I Learn from the Visuals
25	The Olympics is a large competition.	
26		
29		

Think About It

Think about what you have read. Then think about how you can treat others with respect.

Draw It

How can you help people? Draw a picture of a person helping others in the school or community. Write a label for your picture.

Talk About It

Explain

Share your drawing with a partner. Talk about other ways to help people and show respect.

Civics

Connect to the

Take Action

How can you be a good citizen in your town? List three things you could do to be a good citizen in your community.

1. _____

2. _____

3. _____

_____

Inquiry Project Notes

_____

_____

Why Do We Vote?

Lesson Outcomes

What Am I Learning?
You will explore voting and why people vote.

Why Am I Learning It?
You will know why voting is important.

How Will I Know that I Learned It?
You will practice voting in your classroom.

Talk About It

Look closely at the picture.
What is the student doing?
How is he making a choice?

©DSGpro/Getty Images

HSS 1.1.1

These students write down their votes on a piece of paper.

BALLOT BOX

Read Look at the title. What do you think this text will be about?

Circle words you don't know.

Underline clues that tell you:

- What is voting?
- How can people vote?
- Why do people vote?

My Notes

_____

_____

_____

_____

Voting Matters

Voting is making a choice that can be counted. Voting is a way to be fair.

A class wants to name their pet hamster. The choices are Fluffy and Doodle. Each person chooses the name he or she likes best. Each choice is one vote. Every student gets a chance to pick the winning name. The pet name with the most votes wins. Which name do you like best?

These students vote in their classroom.

There are many ways to vote. People can vote in public. They can raise their hands or say their choice.

When Americans vote for leaders, the votes are private. Americans don't have to tell others who they voted for. The leader with the most votes gets to make decisions for the people. Voting is important. Voting is a way that citizens choose leaders fairly.

A voting booth keeps votes private. Others can't see who we choose.

Hill Street Studios/Getty Images

2 Find Evidence

Compare How do the two pictures show the same kind of voting?

Underline the text that tells how this kind of voting is done in America.

3 Make Connections

Talk Good citizens vote for COLLABORATE their leaders. Why do you think this is important? Why is it important for you to vote in your classroom?

Explore

The **topic** is what the text is about.

Key details tell you about the topic of a text.

You can use words and photos to learn key details.

To find the topic and key details:

1. Read the whole text. Decide what the text is about. This is the topic.

2. Look for sentences about the topic. These are key details.

3. Look at the text, pictures, and captions. Underline the key details.

4. Ask yourself, *Do these details tell me important things about the main topic?*

 COLLABORATE Work with your class to complete the chart.

Main Topic: Voting is Important		
Key Detail	Key Detail	Key Detail
Voting is a way to be fair.		

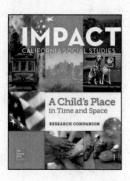

Investigate!

Read pages 30-35 in your Research Companion.

Look for key details about why voting is important.

Write the information in the chart.

Main Topic: Voting is Important		
Key Detail	Key Detail	Key Detail

Think About It

Think about what you have read.
What are the different ways people vote?

Write About It

Define
What is voting?

_____

_____

_____

Cite Evidence
Why do Americans vote?

_____

_____

_____

Talk About It

Explain

Share your response with a partner. Together, discuss some choices the class could make together by voting.

Civics

Connect to the EQ

Take Action

Take a vote. What supplies does your classroom need? As a group, write three things the classroom needs. Then take a class-wide vote. Record the results in a bar graph.

How Have Rights and Responsibilities Changed over Time?

Lesson Outcomes

What Am I Learning?
You will explore rights and responsibilities of the past.

Why Am I Learning It?
You will know how responsibilities and rights have changed over time.

How Will I Know that I Learned It?
You will list rights and responsibilities today that are different from the past.

Talk About It

Look closely at the picture. What responsibilities do these children have when they are in school?

HSS 1.4, HAS.CS.2, HAS.CS.3

38 Lesson 5 How Have Rights and Responsibilities Changed over Time?

1 Inspect

Read Look at the pictures. What do you think this text will be about?

Circle the details that tell you who the text is about.

Highlight the sentences that tell you:

- What did the person do?
- What responsibilities did the person have?

My Notes

_____

_____

_____

Booker T. Washington

In the **past**, African American citizens didn't have many rights. Many African Americans were slaves. Slaves were property. People owned slaves and forced them to work.

Later, African Americans became free American citizens. But they still didn't have many rights. Many could not find jobs or go to school.

Booker T. Washington was an African American citizen. He found a job as a janitor at a school. He worked hard at his job and went to classes. Then he became a teacher.

Booker T. Washington helped African Americans have more rights and responsibilities.

Prints and Photographs Division, Library of Congress, LCOUSZ62-II9897

Booker T. Washington felt a **responsibility** to help others. He started a school for African American students. He helped a new generation of African Americans become teachers. He also helped them grow food and learn other responsibilities of good citizens.

Today, African Americans have the same rights and responsibilities as all American citizens.

Booker T. Washington helped African American teachers and students.

2 Find Evidence

Reread How did the rights and responsibilities of African Americans change?

Underline the words that show these rights and responsibilities.

3 Make Connections

Draw
Look at the pictures on these pages. Draw your own picture to show a right that African Americans did not have in the past.

COLLABORATE

Explore Contrast

When you **contrast**, you think about how things are different.
To contrast details in the text:

1. Read the whole text.

2. Reread the text. Circle words that tell you how things were in the past.

3. Reread the text again. Underline words that tell you how things are today.

COLLABORATE Read the text. Then work with your class to complete the chart.

In the Past	Today
	African Americans have the same rights as all American citizens.

Investigate!

Read pages 36–41 in your Research Companion.

Look for details that tell you about how rights and responsibilities have changed.

Write the details in the chart.

In the Past	Today
	Children can go to school.
People had responsibilities like chopping wood and getting water.	

Think About It

Think about children's responsibilities in the past.
How have those responsibilities changed?

Write About It

Work with a partner to complete the sentences
about rights and responsibilities. Use details from
the texts to help you complete the sentences.

One responsibility children had in the past was _____

_____

_____

_____

One right children have today is _____

_____

_____

_____

Talk About It

Explain

Discuss with a partner how rights and responsibilities have changed over time.

History Connect to the EQ

How have rights and responsibilities changed over time? List three ideas about rights and responsibilities today that are different from the past.

1. _____

_____

2. _____

_____

3. _____

_____

Inquiry Project Wrap Up

Our Classroom Is a Country

Now's the time to discuss your project. Here's what to do.

☐ Talk about the country name. Why did you choose the name?

☐ Describe the parts of your flag. Tell how you chose them.

☐ Discuss your rule. What makes this rule the **best** one?

☐ Talk about how well you think it worked. Describe what you accomplished.

Tips for Discussing

Use these words to talk with classmates about their work:

☐ I notice . . .

☐ I think . . .

☐ I wonder . . .

☐ I agree, because . . .

Project Rubric

Use these questions to help evaluate your project.

	Yes	No
Is our project complete, with a name, a flag, and a rule?		
Does our flag tell about our country?		
Will our rule help people be good citizens in our country?		
Did we work well as a team?		

Project Reflection

Think about the work you did in this chapter, either with a group or on your own. Describe something you think you did very well. What would you do differently?

_____

_____

_____

_____

Goldilocks and the Three Bears

Narrator: Goldilocks went to visit the three bears. But they were not home.

Goldilocks: I will go inside and wait for them.

Narrator: Goldilocks went inside.

Groups A and B: Yum! Three bowls of soup!

Goldilocks: Should I eat some of this tasty soup?

Narrator: Goldilocks was hungry. But she wasn't sure about eating the soup.

Narrator: Goldilocks decided to eat a bowl of soup. Then the bears came home!

Papa Bear: Hello, Goldilocks! Sorry we are late.

Mama Bear: Have you been waiting a long time?

Baby Bear: Hey! Someone ate my soup!

Narrator: Baby bear started to cry.

Goldilocks: I'm sorry, Baby Bear. It was me. I ate your soup.

Mama Bear: You should not take what isn't yours, Goldilocks. That is a rule in this house.

Goldilocks: I'm sorry. I did not know the rule.

Papa Bear: It's okay, Baby Bear, you can have my soup.

Baby Bear: Thanks, Papa!

Goldilocks: I feel bad about eating Baby Bear's soup.

Group A: Do something nice for Baby Bear!

Group B: You should make more soup. That will cheer up Baby Bear!

Goldilocks: Papa Bear, would you teach me how to make soup? I want to make some more.

Papa Bear: That's a good idea, Goldilocks. I will show you how. Then we can all have soup. I hope you learned not to take what isn't yours.

Goldilocks: I sure did. Let's make more soup!

Narrator: They made a big pot of soup and ate it together.

Groups A and B: It was yummy!

Our Community

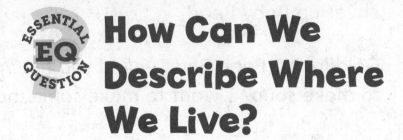

How Can We Describe Where We Live?

In this chapter, you'll explore places in your community and around the world. You'll learn how to find places using a map or globe. You'll also work with a team on a chapter project to create a flipbook of your community.

Talk About It COLLABORATE

Discuss your favorite place to visit in your community with a partner.

My Research Questions

1._____

_____

2._____

_____

HSS 1.2, HSS 1.2.1, HSS 1.2.2, HSS 1.2.3, HSS 1.2.4, HSS 1.3.1, HSS 1.6.2, HAS.CS.1.1, HAS.CS.1.4, HAS.CS.1.5, HAS.HR.1.2, HAS.HI.1.2

Inquiry Project

My Community

In this project, you'll work with a team to create flipbooks of places in your community.

Here's your project checklist.

☐ **Label** each page in your flipbook with the following sentences:

- I live on planet Earth.
- I live in the continent of North America.
- I live in the United States.
- I live in California.
- I live in the city of _____.
- My address is _____.

☐ **Discuss** what makes the place where you live different. List some special places or buildings in your community.

☐ **Brainstorm** about what you will draw on each page. Think about some things to add in each picture.

☐ **Draw** a picture for each sentence in the flipbook.

☐ **Present** your flipbook to the class. Share what is special about your community.

Explore Words

Complete this chapter's Word Rater. Write notes as you learn more about each word.

address   My Notes

☐ Know It! _____

☐ Heard It!

☐ Don't Know It! _____

border   My Notes

☐ Know It! _____

☐ Heard It!

☐ Don't Know It! _____

capital   My Notes

☐ Know It! _____

☐ Heard It!

☐ Don't Know It! _____

continent   My Notes

☐ Know It! _____

☐ Heard It!

☐ Don't Know It! _____

environment My Notes

☐ Know It! _____

☐ Heard It!

☐ Don't Know It! _____

globe

My Notes

☐ Know It!
☐ Heard It!
☐ Don't Know It!

_____

_____

location

My Notes

☐ Know It!
☐ Heard It!
☐ Don't Know It!

_____

_____

neighborhood

My Notes

☐ Know It!
☐ Heard It!
☐ Don't Know It!

_____

_____

symbols

My Notes

☐ Know It!
☐ Heard It!
☐ Don't Know It!

_____

_____

transportation

My Notes

☐ Know It!
☐ Heard It!
☐ Don't Know It!

_____

_____

What Does a Map Help Us Do?

Lesson Outcomes

What Am I Learning?
You will explore how maps help us.

Why Am I Learning It?
You will draw a map that shows places in your neighborhood.

How Will I Know that I Learned It?
You will list places in your neighborhood that you have visited and show them on a map.

Talk About It

Look closely at the model, map, and photo. What do they show? How are they different?

Playground Map

This map shows different places in a playground.

The photo shows places in a real playground.

1 Inspect

Look closely at the photo and map.

Circle something that is the same in the photo and the map.

My Notes

_____

_____

_____

_____

_____

_____

What Maps Show

This photo was taken high above a **neighborhood**. A neighborhood is a place where people live, work, play, and shop.

What places do you see in this neighborhood?

fotog/Getty Images

A map shows where places are located. Maps help you know how to get from place to place.

Pine Lane

Broad Court

Front Court

This is a map. It shows the same neighborhood that you see in the photo.

2 Find Evidence

Reread How can a map be more helpful than a photo?

Circle something on the map that is not in the photo.

3 Make Connections

Talk How are the photo and the map alike? How are they different?

Turn back to page 57. How does the map help you understand the playground?

Explore Map and Globe Skills

A **map** is a drawing that shows a place.

To read a map:

1. Look at the title. The title tells what the map shows.

2. Look for labels. These tell you about important parts of the map.

3. Look for other information. The map might show street names or buildings.

COLLABORATE

Work with your class to fill in the graphic organizer with details from the maps and text.

Map Feature (What You See on a Map)	How It Helps
Street names	

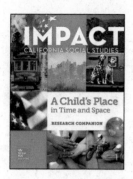

Investigate!

Read pages 50–57 in your Research Companion.

Look for clues that tell you what each feature of a map does.

Write your information in the graphic organizer.

Map Feature (What You See on a Map)	How It Helps
Title	
Label	
Compass Rose	
Cardinal Directions	
Map Key	
Symbol	

Think About It

How would you show places in your neighborhood on a map?

Draw

Draw a map that shows places in your neighborhood.
Use symbols and a map key. Add a compass rose.

Talk About It

Explain

Share your map with a partner. Tell your partner about places in your neighborhood.

 **Connect to the EQ**

Geography

Take Action

List three things that a map can help us do.

1. _____

_____

2. _____

_____

3. _____

_____

_____

What Can We Learn From Different Kinds of Maps?

Lesson Outcomes

What Am I Learning?
You will learn about different kinds of maps.

Why Am I Learning It?
You will be able to draw a map of California.

How Will I Know that I Learned it?
You will show when to use different kinds of maps.

Talk About It COLLABORATE

Look closely at the picture.
What are the children doing?
What can you use maps for?

Maps can teach us many different things about a place.

Read Look at the title. What do you think you will learn?

Circle California on the map.

Highlight the capital of California.

Underline clues that tell you:

- what a political map shows.
- what a capital city is.

My Notes

_____

_____

_____

Political Maps

Political maps show borders of states. They also show borders of countries. **Borders** are the lines around a state or country. They show where one place ends and another begins.

A political map also shows bodies of water. It shows a state's large cities and capital city. The **capital** city has state government offices.

This political map shows the borders of California. California shares borders with other states. California also shares a border with Mexico.

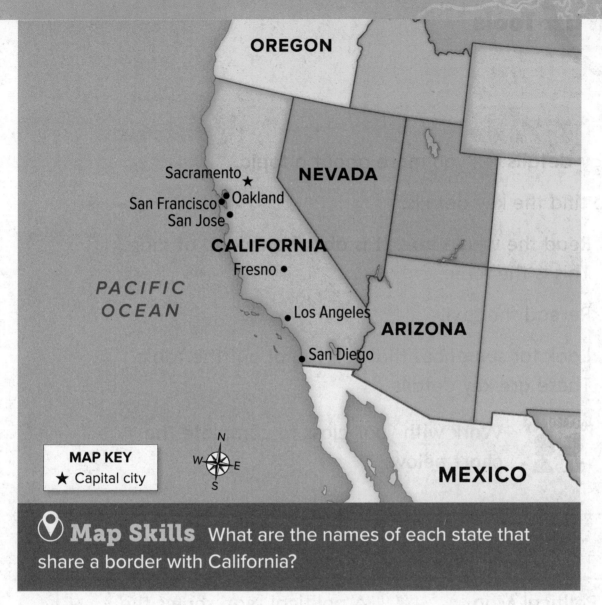

OREGON

Sacramento ★

San Francisco ● ● Oakland

San Jose ●

NEVADA

CALIFORNIA

Fresno ●

PACIFIC OCEAN

Los Angeles ●

ARIZONA

San Diego ●

MEXICO

MAP KEY
★ Capital city

N
W E
S

📍 **Map Skills** What are the names of each state that share a border with California?

A political map shows the capital city of a state. Sacramento is the capital city of California.

2 Find Evidence

Reread How do borders on a political map help you know more about a state?

Circle the name of the country that is on California's border to the south.

3 Make Connections

Talk What states share a border with California?

Explore Key Details

Key details tell you more about a topic.

To find the key details:

1. Read the whole text. It is about one kind of map. This is the topic.

2. Reread the text.

3. Look for sentences that tell you about the topic. These are key details.

 COLLABORATE Work with your class to complete the chart below.

Type of Map	Key Detail About the Map
Political Map	A political map shows the _____ between states and countries.

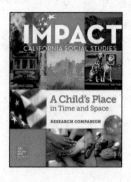

Investigate!

Read pages 58-63 in your Research Companion.

Look for key details about different types of maps.

Type of Map	Key Detail About the Map
Physical Map	A physical map shows different types of _____ and _____.
Product Map	A product map shows where things are _____ or _____.
Weather Map	A weather map can use _____ to show what the weather is like.

Think About It

Think about what you read. Why do people use different types of maps?

Draw A Map

Use the map outline to draw your own map of California. Add the state name and capital city.

Use symbols and a map key to show water and land. What other details can you add?

Talk About It

Explain

Share your map with a partner. Tell your partner what the symbols show.

Geography

Connect to the

Use Different Maps

What can we learn from using different types of maps? Work with a partner. Draw lines to show what type of map you would use to find the information listed below.

Information	Type of Map
Find out where strawberries are produced.	Weather Map
Find out if it will rain where you live.	Physical Map
Find out the capital city of your state.	Product Map
Find out where a lake is located.	Political Map

How Do We Use Maps and Globes?

Lesson Outcomes

What Am I Learning?

You will learn how maps and globes are alike and different.

Why Am I Learning it?

You will know when to use a map and when to use a globe.

How Will I Know that I Learned it?

You will explain what maps and globes show us about where we live.

Talk About It

Look closely at the picture. What are the girls doing? Why do you think they are doing this?

HSS.1.2.2

A globe shows us what Earth looks like.

Analyze the Source

1 Inspect

Read Look at the pictures. How are they alike? How are they different?

Circle the land and water in both pictures.

Draw arrows to point to things that are in one picture and not in the other.

My Notes

_____

_____

_____

_____

_____

What Is A Globe?

Look at this picture of Earth from space. Look at the globe. A **globe** is a model of Earth in the shape of a ball. A globe shows the whole Earth.

This is a picture of Earth from space.

©Stocktrek/Getty Images

The picture of Earth shows land and water. It also shows clouds. The globe uses different colors to show land. Each country is shown in a different color.

The globe also shows the equator. The equator is an imaginary line around the middle of the globe.

A globe shows the equator.

Brand X/SuperStock

2 Find Evidence

Look What can you learn about Earth from a globe?

Underline words that teach you about Earth.

3 Make Connections

Talk How are the picture of Earth and the globe alike? How are they different?

COLLABORATE

Explore Compare and Contrast

When you **compare**, you think about how things are alike.

When you **contrast**, you think about how things are different.

To compare and contrast:

1. Read the whole text.

2. Circle words that tell you how things are alike.

3. Underline words that tell you how things are different.

COLLABORATE   Work with your class to complete the graphic organizer below.

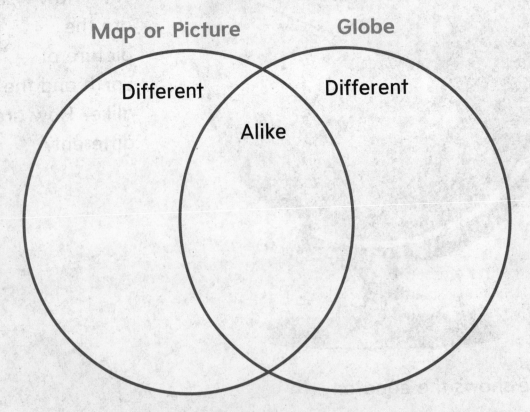

Map or Picture   Globe

Different   Different

Alike

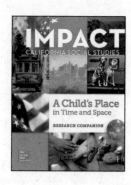

Investigate!

Read pages 64–69 in your Research Companion.

Look for clues that tell you how maps and globes are alike and different.

Write your information in the graphic organizer.

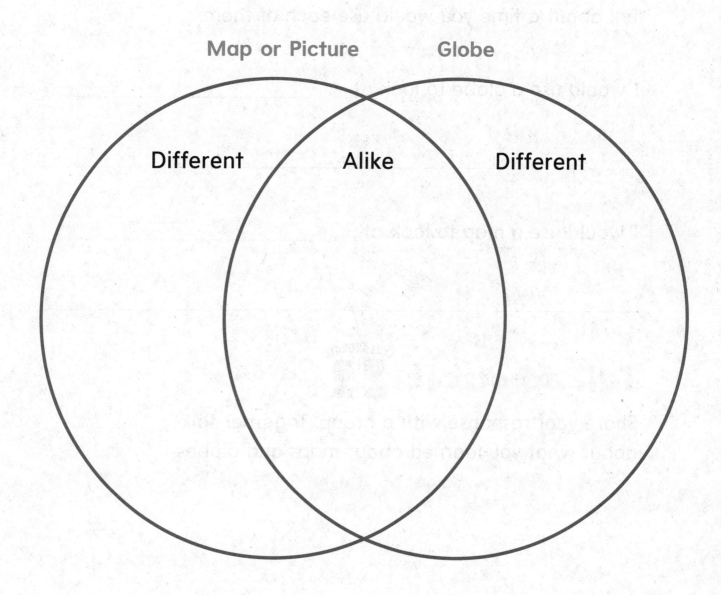

Map or Picture   Globe

Different   Alike   Different

Think About It

Think about what you read. How do globes and maps help us understand location?

Write About It

When would you use a globe? When would you use a map?

Tell about a time you would use each of them.

I would use a globe to look at _____

_____

I would use a map to look at _____

_____

Talk About It   COLLABORATE

Share your response with a group. Together talk about what you learned about maps and globes.

Connect to the **EQ**

Geography

ESSENTIAL QUESTION

Should I Use a Map or a Globe?

Your friend wants to find the city's library. Should she use a map or a globe? Give your friend some advice.

_____

_____

_____

_____

_____

_____

_____

Where is Our Community in the World?

Lesson Outcomes

What Am I Learning?

You will explore different ways to locate and talk about your community.

Why Am I Learning it?

You will show where your community is located within your state.

How Will I Know that I Learned it?

You will describe your community and explain where it is located.

Talk About It

COLLABORATE

Look closely at the photos. What are the children doing? How do you know?

1 Inspect

Read Look at the title. What do you think this text will be about?

Underline words that explain what an address can tell us.

Circle words that explain what an address needs to show.

My Notes

_____

_____

_____

_____

My Address

It's fun to get a card in the mail! How does the card get to you? The sender needs to know your address.

An **address** tells where people live or work. An address gives an exact **location**.

An address should have a number to tell which house or building. An address also tells what street or road a house or building is on. It also needs a city or town. It needs a state, too.

Lin Potts
316 Elm Street
Apt. B-5
Fresno, CA 93704

CA is a short way to write *California*.

Jack is sending cards to his friends. He wrote each name on the first line of the address.

Ben lives in the small town of Auburn. He lives on a quiet road. His zip code tells us where his town is located.

Kaylie lives in the busy city. Her address has an apartment number. Kaylie's building has many apartments.

Marita Lee
600 Park Street
Montrose, CA 91020

Ben Jackson
152 Hill Road
Auburn, CA 95602

Kaylie Boyle
7522 Channel Ave., Apt. 4
Los Angeles, CA 90007

The parts of an address tell postal workers where to deliver mail.

2 Find Evidence

Reread How do the pictures help you understand the parts of an address?

Underline the street name, town, and state for each address.

3 Make Connections

Talk Why is each part of an address important? What might happen if you forgot to write part of an address?

Explore Main Topic and Key Details

The **main topic** is what the text is about.

Key details give information about the main topic.

To find the main topic and key details:

1. Read title and the text.

2. Decide what the text is about. This is the main topic. Circle it.

3. Look for details that give information about the main topic. Underline two or three key details.

4. Ask yourself: *Does the title give a clue about the main topic?*

 COLLABORATE Work with your class to complete the graphic organizer below.

Key Details: My address tells people what city I live in.

Key Details:

Topic: My Address

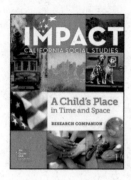

Investigate!

Read pages 70-77 in your Research Companion.

Look for key details about communities and where your community is located.

Write your information in the graphic organizer.

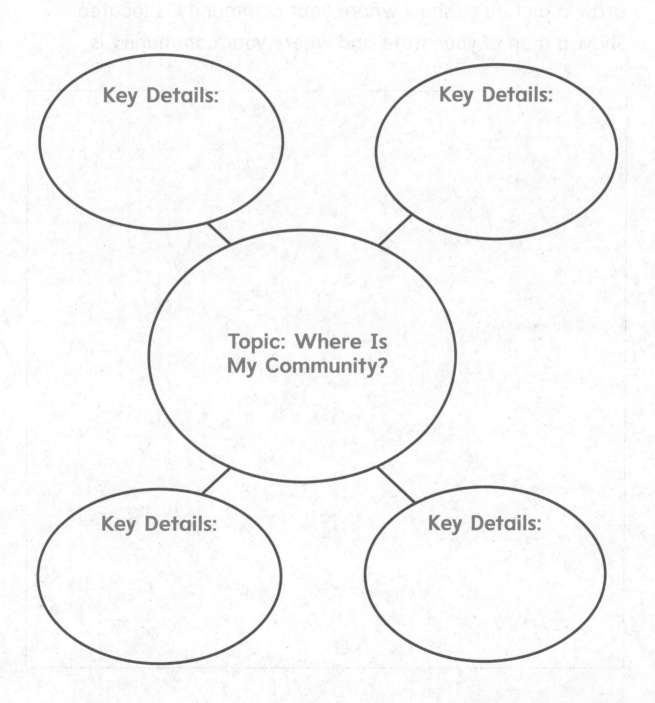

Key Details:

Key Details:

Topic: Where Is My Community?

Key Details:

Key Details:

Think About It

Think about what you just read about communities. Where is your community?

Draw It

Draw a picture to show where your community is located. Show a map of your state and where your community is.

Talk About It

COLLABORATE

Explain

Share your response with a partner. Talk about what your community is like. Where is it located? How is it different from other communities?

Civics

Connect to the EQ

ESSENTIAL QUESTION

Describe

Complete the three sentences to describe your community.

1. The name of my community is _____

_____.

2. My community is located _____

_____.

3. My community is special because _____

_____.

How Do Location and Weather Affect Us?

Lesson Outcomes

What Am I Learning?
You will learn about weather and environment in different parts of the world.

Why Am I Learning It?
You will understand more about the weather in your own community.

How Will I Know that I Learned It?
You will write about how location and weather affect life in your community.

Talk About It   COLLABORATE

Look closely at the two pictures. What do you think the weather is like in each place? How do you know?

HSS 1.2.4; HAS.CS.5; HAS.HI.2

1 Inspect

Read Look at the title and picture captions. What do you think this text will be about?

Circle words you don't know.

Underline the differences between the environments in northern California and southern California.

My Notes

_____

_____

_____

_____

How We Live

A location is a place. Different locations have different environments. An **environment** is the nature that surrounds a living thing. Is your community near the ocean or the mountains? Maybe it is near a forest or a desert.

The environment also affects how people live. Food, clothes, homes, and transportation may be different in different places. **Transportation** is the way people move from place to place.

These children live where it is cold. They like to play in the snow.

©Purestock/PunchStock

These children live where it is hot. They like to play in the water.

Northern California has many green forests and mountains. People can go hiking or climbing. In the winter, they can snowboard or ski.

Southern California has more desert areas. The beaches are warm and sunny. Even in the winter, people can swim or surf in the ocean.

2 Find Evidence

Reread Why is outdoor fun sometimes different in northern and southern California?

Underline clues that support what you think.

3 Make Connections

Draw Make a picture that COLLABORATE shows how you have fun where you live. Show what you do and what you wear.

Now draw a picture that shows how you would have fun in a different environment. How would your clothing and activity change?

Explore Cause and Effect

The **effect** is what happens.

The **cause** is why it happens.

To find the cause and effect:

1. Read the whole text.

2. Look for something that tells you what happens. This is an effect. Circle it.

3. Look for a detail that tells you why it happens. This is a cause. Underline it.

4. Ask yourself: *Did one thing make another thing happen?*

 COLLABORATE Work with your class to complete the graphic organizer below.

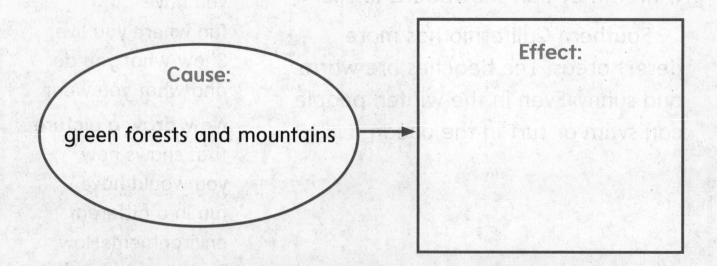

Cause:

green forests and mountains

Effect:

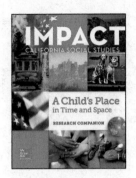

Investigate!

Read pages 78-87 in your Research Companion.

Look for details that tell you what happens and why it happens.

Write your information in the graphic organizer.

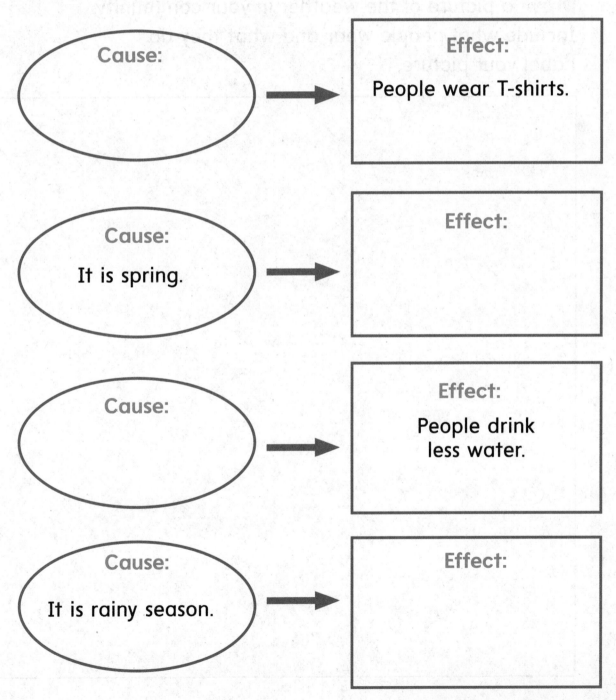

Cause:

Effect:
People wear T-shirts.

Cause:
It is spring.

Effect:

Cause:

Effect:
People drink
less water.

Cause:
It is rainy season.

Effect:

Think About It

What is the weather like in your community?
How does it change?

Write About It

Draw a picture of the weather in your community.
Include what people wear and what they do.
Label your picture.

Talk About It

Explain

Share your responses with a partner. Together, discuss how location, weather, and environment affect your lives.

Geography

Connect to the **EQ**

Talk with a group. How do location and weather affect life in your community? Ask your teacher to make a list of your answers.

1. Location _____

_____

2. Weather _____

_____

3. Environment _____

_____

_____

_____

Inquiry Project Wrap Up

My Community

Now's the time for your team to share your project with the rest of the class. Here's what to do.

☐ Share your list of places with the class.

☐ Explain why each place in the flipbook is special.

☐ Talk about what makes your community different from other communities.

☐ Show the pictures in your flipbook.

Tips for Presenting

Remember these tips when you present to your class.

☐ Practice what you will say.

☐ Speak loudly and clearly.

☐ Display your flipbook so everyone can see.

☐ Answer your classmates' questions.

Project Rubric

Use these questions to help evaluate your project.

	Yes	No
Did we follow the checklist?		
Is our writing neat and clear?		
Do the pictures show what makes our community special?		
Is our flipbook colorful and interesting?		
Did we work well as a team?		

Project Reflection

Think about the work that you did in this chapter, either with a group or on your own. Describe something that you think you did very well. What would you do differently?

_____

_____

_____

_____

Country Cousin, City Cousin

CHARACTERS

City Cousin
Country Cousin
Taxi Cabs
Fruit Seller
Owls
Frogs
Narrator

Narrator: City Cousin liked the sounds of the city.

Taxi Cabs: Honk! Beep! ZOOM!

City Cousin: I also like buying fruit on the street.

Fruit Seller: Apples for sale! Oranges for sale!
Bananas for sale!

City Cousin: I like the city. But I need a break.

Narrator: City Cousin knew just where to go. He got on a train and went to see Country Cousin.

Country Cousin: Hi! I live in the country. I like big fields and quiet rivers. Sometimes I hear owls and frogs at night.

Owls: Hoot, hoot!

Frogs: Ribbet! Ribbet!

Country Cousin: I like playing in the woods. I can be as loud as I want.

Narrator: Country Cousin picked up City Cousin at the train station.

City Cousin: Hi cousin! It is good to see you. I need a break from city life.

Country Cousin: Well, let's go for a walk and enjoy the quiet!

Narrator: The cousins walked down a country lane. It was very quiet.

Owls: Hoot, hoot, HOOT!!!

City Cousin: What was that?!

Country Cousin: It was only an owl. I like the sound of hooting owls.

City Cousin: We don't have owls where I live. I'm not used to that sound.

Narrator: They kept walking. City Cousin was a little scared.

Frogs: Ribbet! RIBBET!

City Cousin: What was that?!

Country Cousin: It's just some frogs.

City Cousin: I thought it would be quiet here in the country.

Country Cousin: Well, we have our own sounds.

City Cousin: Yes, and it's still quieter than the city.

Country Cousin: Come on, cousin. Let's get something to eat!

City Cousin: Sure! But where are all the people selling fruit?

Country Cousin: In the country, we pick our own fruit.

Narrator: The cousins stopped at an apple tree. They picked armfuls of apples. They went home and made a pie for dessert.

City Cousin: That pie was tasty! I like life in the country.

Country Cousin: I'll visit you in the city next time. You can take me for a taxi cab ride!

Chapter 3

Celebrating America

How Do We Celebrate Our Country?

In this chapter, you'll explore how we celebrate our country. You'll read about how Americans remember important events and people from America's history. You'll also work with a team on a chapter project to make a Big Book of important things about America.

Talk About It

COLLABORATE

Discuss with a partner what questions you have about how we celebrate our country.

My Research Questions

1. _____

_____

2. _____

_____

HSS 1.1.2, HSS 1.3, HSS 1.3.1, HSS 1.3.2, HSS 1.3.3, HSS 1.4.3, HSS 1.5.2, HAS.CS.1.1, HAS.HR.1.2, HAS.HI.1.1, HAS.HI.1.3

Inquiry Project

Big Book of Important Symbols

In this project, you'll work with a team to make a Big Book of all the national and state symbols you learn about in the chapter. Some of these symbols will be objects, and some of them will be monuments or buildings.

Here's your project checklist.

☐ **Collect** the names of every state and national symbol you find in the chapter.

☐ **Draw** a picture of each symbol that you find. Be sure to label your drawings with the name of the symbol.

☐ **Think** about what the symbol means. Why is this symbol important in celebrating our country?

☐ **Make** a book out of your drawings. Make sure all the drawings are labeled, and every symbol has a description of what it means and why it is important.

☐ **Present** your Big Book to the class. Listen to the other groups as they present their Big Books.

Explore Words

Complete this chapter's Word Rater. Write notes as you learn more about each word.

amendment   My Notes

☐ Know It!   _____

☐ Heard It!   _____

☐ Don't Know It! _____

celebrate   My Notes

☐ Know It!   _____

☐ Heard It!   _____

☐ Don't Know It! _____

colony   My Notes

☐ Know It!   _____

☐ Heard It!   _____

☐ Don't Know It! _____

document   My Notes

☐ Know It!   _____

☐ Heard It!   _____

☐ Don't Know It! _____

government   My Notes

- ☐ Know It!
- ☐ Heard It!
- ☐ Don't Know It!

_____

_____

_____

holiday   My Notes

- ☐ Know It!
- ☐ Heard It!
- ☐ Don't Know It!

_____

_____

_____

independence   My Notes

- ☐ Know It!
- ☐ Heard It!
- ☐ Don't Know It!

_____

_____

_____

monument   My Notes

- ☐ Know It!
- ☐ Heard It!
- ☐ Don't Know It!

_____

_____

_____

Lesson 1

Why Do Americans Celebrate Independence Day?

Lesson Outcomes

What Am I Learning?
You will find out why Americans celebrate Independence Day.

Why Am I Learning It?
You will write about why Independence Day is an important holiday.

How Will I Know that I Learned It?
You will tell others about Independence Day and why we celebrate it.

Talk About It COLLABORATE

Look closely at the picture. What do you think these men are doing? When did this happen? How do you know?

The founding fathers signed the Declaration of Independence in 1776.

1 Inspect

Read Look at the title and captions. What do you think this text will be about?

Circle words you don't know.

Underline words that tell you:

- which country ruled the colonies.
- who made laws for the people in the colonies.
- what the colonists wanted.

My Notes

_____

_____

_____

The Thirteen Colonies

The United States began as a group of colonies. A **colony** is a place that belongs to a different country. England ruled the colonies. The King of England made the laws for the people who lived there.

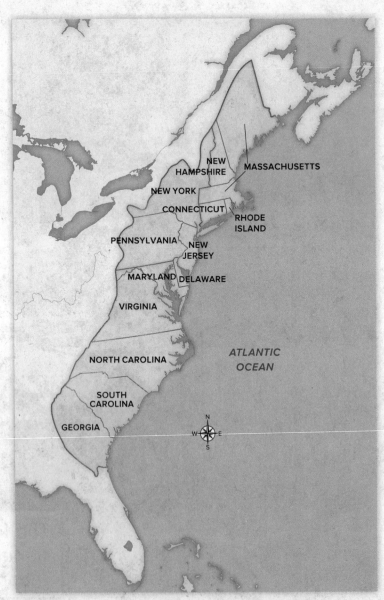

Long ago, England ruled the 13 colonies.

Leaders talked with colonists about how to gain independence from England.

The King of England made choices for the people in the colonies. The people had to pay money to England. They did not have the same rights as the people in England.

Many colonists were unhappy. They did not like paying money to a country so far away. They wanted to make their own laws. Leaders in the colonies discussed **independence**. Independence is freedom from being controlled by others.

2 Find Evidence

Reread Why were many colonists unhappy?

Underline clues that explain what the colonists didn't like.

3 Make Connections

Talk What did the colonists want to change? How do you think talking to each other helped?

Explore Sequence

Sequence is the order in which things happen.

To find the **sequence:**

1. Read the whole text.

2. Find out what happened first.

3. Look for what happened next and after that.

4. Find out what happened last.

Ask yourself: *Did I find the important things that happened? Can I retell them in the right order?*

COLLABORATE Work with your class to complete the graphic organizer below.

Topic: The Colonies of England

First England was in charge of colonies.

↓

Next The colonists had to _____ to England.

↓

Then Colonists wanted to make their own _____.

↓

Last _____ got together to talk about the problem.

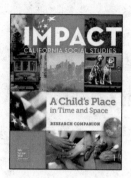

Investigate!

Read pages 98–105 in your Research Companion.

Look for details that tell you the order in which things happened.

Write your information in the graphic organizer.

Topic: How Independence Day Became a Holiday

First

Leaders wrote the _____.

↓

Next

The colonies and _____ went to war.

↓

Next

The colonies became _____.

↓

Last

Independence Day is a holiday to celebrate _____.

Think About It

Think about what you have read. What makes Independence Day a special holiday for Americans?

Write About It

Define

What is independence?

_____

_____

Write and Cite Evidence

Why is Independence Day an important holiday?
Use information from the text to explain.

_____

_____

_____

_____

Talk About It

Explain

Share your thoughts with a partner. Discuss why we celebrate this holiday and why it is special.

Civics Connect to the EQ

Take Action

Pretend you have a pen pal who lives in another country. Write a note about Independence Day. Tell your pen pal how Independence Day is a way to celebrate our country.

_____

_____

_____

_____

_____

Lesson 2

How Does the Constitution Help Our Country?

Lesson Outcomes

What Am I Learning?

You will learn about how the United States government works.

Why Am I Learning It?

You will be able to tell why the Constitution is important.

How Will I Know that I Learned It?

You will be able to explain how the Constitution helps our country.

Talk About It

Read the words at the top of the Constitution. What do they say? Why do you think the Constitution begins with these words?

The pages of the Constitution are on display in Washington, D.C.

Read Look at the title. What do you think this lesson will be about?

Circle words you don't know.

Underline clues that tell you:

- what the Constitution is.
- who serves in the Congress.
- who makes sure laws are fair.

My Notes

_____

_____

_____

Three Branches of Government

Long ago, leaders wrote the Constitution. The Constitution is the set of rules that explains how the **government** works. The government is a group of people who makes decisions for a state or country.

The leaders created a government with three branches, or parts.

- Congress is a group of leaders from each state. They make laws.

- The president makes sure that people follow laws.

- The Supreme Court makes sure laws are fair.

The web shows the three branches of government. All the branches must work together to make sure the government works well.

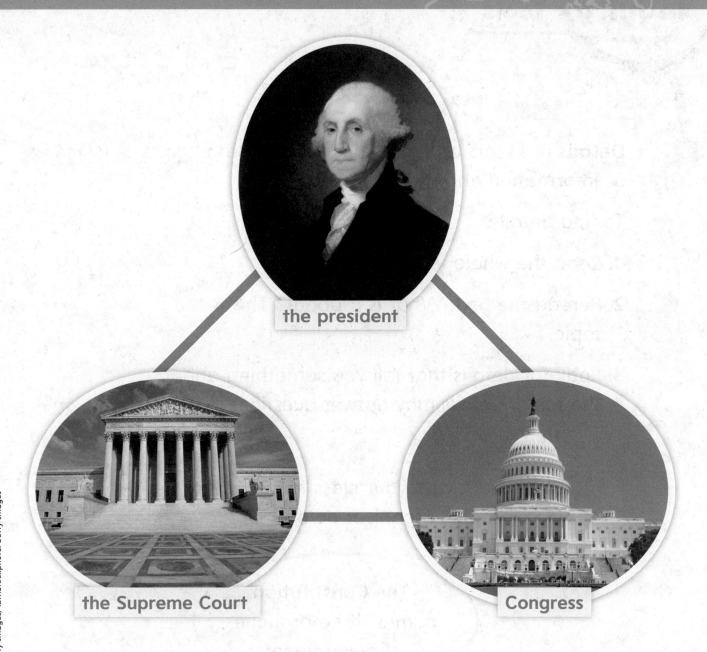

the president

the Supreme Court

Congress

2 Find Evidence

Reread How does the web help you understand the United States government?

Underline the job that each branch does.

3 Make Connections

Write

What job does each branch of the government do?

Explore Details

Details are facts and statements. Each detail gives us information about the topic.

To find details:

1. Read the whole text.

2. Reread the text. What is it about? This is the topic.

3. Look for details that tell you something about the topic. Details may answer questions like *Who? What? When? Why?*

 COLLABORATE Work with your class to complete the graphic organizer below.

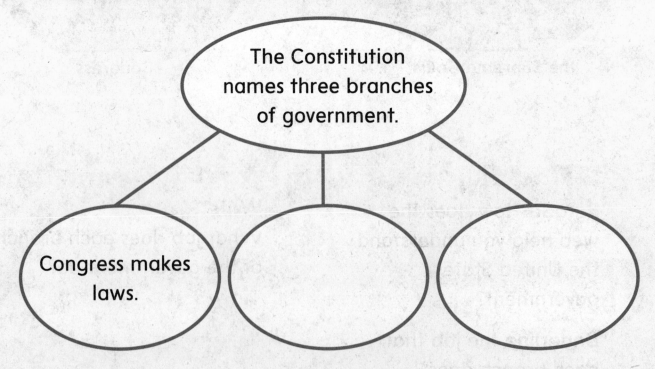

The Constitution names three branches of government.

Congress makes laws.

Investigate!

Read pages 106–111 in your Research Companion.

Look for details that tell you more about the government and the Constitution.

Write your information in the graphic organizer.

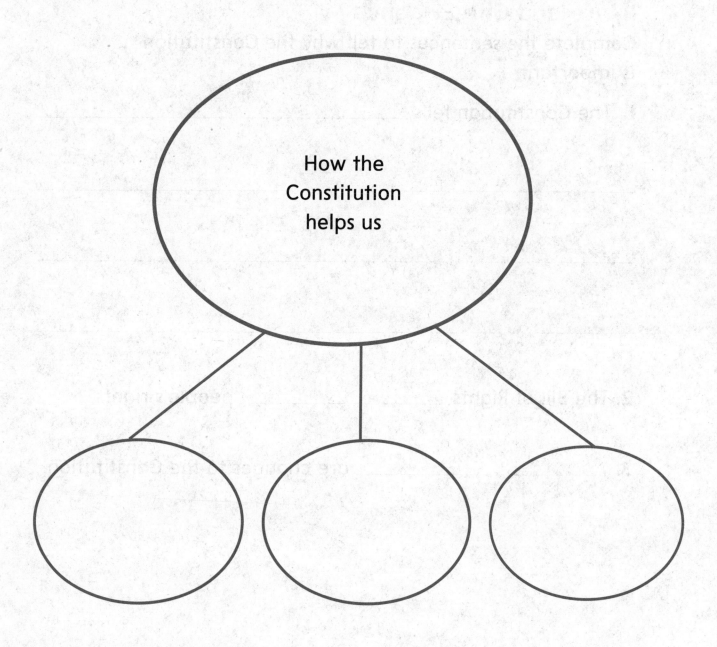

How the
Constitution
helps us

Think About It

Think about what you have read.
Why is the Constitution important?

Write About It

Write and Cite Evidence

Complete the sentences to tell why the Constitution
is important.

I. The Constitution tells _____

_____

_____

2. The Bill of Rights _____ people's rights.

3. _____ are changes to the Constitution.

Talk About It

Explain

Share your writing with your partner.
Discuss why the Constitution is important.

Connect to the

Citizenship

Opinion

What would our country be like without the Constitution?
Write one thing that would be different.

_____

_____

_____

Inquiry Project Notes

_____

_____

_____

What Do Our National and State Symbols Mean?

Lesson Outcomes

What Am I Learning?
You will learn about the symbols that stand for our country and state.

Why Am I Learning It?
You will choose your favorite symbol and tell about why you like it.

How Will I Know that I Learned It?
You will make a new symbol for our country and tell others about it.

Talk About It

Look at the picture of the flag. This flag is a symbol that stands for something. What does it stand for?

HSS 1.3.1, HSS 1.3.3

Pledge of Allegiance

1 Inspect

Look at the picture. What do you think this text will be about?

Read the words. **Circle** words you don't know.

Underline clues that tell you what the people are saying.

My Notes

_____

_____

_____

_____

_____

I pledge allegiance
to the flag of the
United States of
America,
and to the Republic for
which it stands,
one Nation under God,
indivisible,
with liberty and
justice for all.

How are the students showing respect for the flag?

2 Find Evidence

Talk What do you think the word *indivisible* means?

Reread the text.

Circle words that tell what our flag stands for.

3 Make Connections

Talk How does saying the Pledge of Allegiance make you feel?

Explore Main Topic and Details

The **main topic** is what the text is about.

Details tell you more about the main topic.

To find the topic and details:

1. Read the title on each page. This is the topic of the text.

2. Read the text. Look for details that tell about the topic.

3. Look at the picture. Pictures can help show the topic or details of a text.

 COLLABORATE Work with your class to complete the graphic organizer.

Symbol	What It Means
American flag	

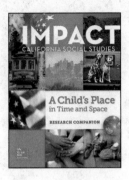

Investigate!

Read pages 112–121 in your Research Companion.

Look for details about symbols.

Write your information in the graphic organizer.

Symbol	What It Means
	Our country gives freedom and hope.
Bald eagle	
	California is a beautiful place.
Grizzly bear	

Think About It

Think about what you read. What symbols are important in the United States?

Write About It

Pick a symbol you read about in this lesson. Which one is your favorite? Write about why you like this symbol.

_____

_____

_____

_____

_____

_____

Talk About It

COLLABORATE

Explain

Share the symbol you chose with a partner.
Ask your partner about his or her symbol.

History

Connect to the

ESSENTIAL QUESTION

EQ

?

Take Action

You can make a new symbol for our country! What does it look like? What does it mean? Why is it important?

1. My symbol looks like _____

_____

2. It means _____

_____

3. It is important because _____

_____

What Do Monuments Help Us Remember?

Lesson Outcomes

What Am I Learning?
You will explore what monuments are and why they are important.

Why Am I Learning It?
You will write about what one monument helps us to remember.

How Will I Know that I Learned It?
You will use what you learned to choose a monument you'd like to visit.

Talk About It

Look closely at the picture. What kind of building do you think this is? Why would people visit this building?

HSS 1.3

Monuments and Memorials

Some buildings or statues are **monuments**. A monument is a building or statue that honors something or someone. We make monuments to help us remember important people and events.

Sometimes monuments are called memorials. Like monuments, memorials honor someone or a group of people. The Lincoln Memorial honors President Abraham Lincoln.

Did You Know?

There are monuments and memorials in every state in the US.

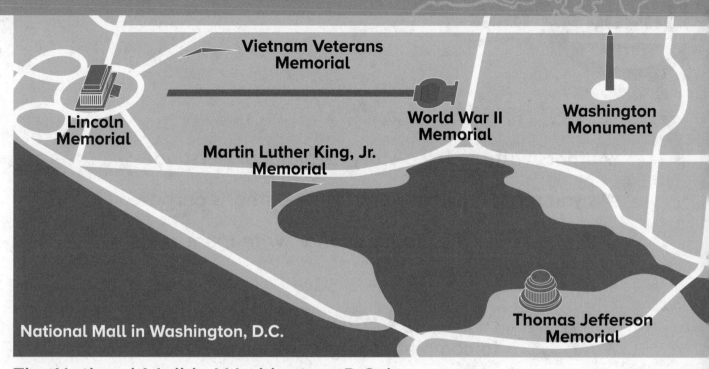

Vietnam Veterans Memorial

Lincoln Memorial

Martin Luther King, Jr. Memorial

World War II Memorial

Washington Monument

Thomas Jefferson Memorial

National Mall in Washington, D.C.

The National Mall in Washington, D.C. has many monuments that help us remember important Americans.

2 Find Evidence

Look closely again. Which monuments and memorials help us remember a person?

Which monuments and memorials help us remember an event?

How do you know? Use the details from the map to help you answer.

3 Make Connections

Talk Turn back to page 133.

Which president was the monument in the picture built for? Use the map to help you answer.

Explore Author's Purpose

Authors write to tell a story, explain, or persuade.

As you read, look for clues to the author's purpose.

Ask yourself, *Why did the author write these words or choose these pictures?*

COLLABORATE As you read, work with your class to complete the graphic organizer.

Clue	Clue	Clue
The map shows the location of monuments.	The map shows _____ _____.	Washington, D.C. has _____ _____.

Author's Purpose

to tell information _____.

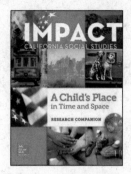

Investigate!

Read pages 122-129 in your Research Companion.

Look for clues that tell you the author's purpose.

Write the clues in your graphic organizer.

Clue	Clue	Clue
Monuments of Abraham Lincoln and George Washington remind us _____ _____ _____ .	Mount Rushmore reminds us _____ _____ _____ _____ .	Monuments around the world remind people _____ _____ _____ .

Author's Purpose

Think About It

Think about your research. Why are monuments important?

Write About It

Choose a monument you read about. Draw a picture or write two sentences about it.

If you draw your monument, be sure to label it. If you write about your monument, tell what it helps us remember. Use details from the text.

Talk About It
COLLABORATE

Share your writing or drawing in a small group.
What new information did you learn?

⛪ Connect to the EQ ESSENTIAL QUESTION
Civics

Which monument do you think is the best to visit?
Write the name of the monument and two reasons.

_____

_____

_____

_____

_____

_____

_____

Lesson 5

How Do We Celebrate Important People and Events?

Lesson Outcomes

What Am I Learning?
You will learn what it means to celebrate people and events.

Why Am I Learning It?
You will understand why we have holidays.

How Will I Know that I Learned It?
You will write about a holiday and its meaning.

Talk About It

Look closely at these pictures. What do you think the people are doing? Why are they doing this? How can you tell?

HSS 1.3.2

140   Lesson 5   How Do We Celebrate Important People and Events?

People often eat special meals and have parades to celebrate holidays.

(t)Monkey Business/Getty Images; (b)digidreamgrafix/Shutterstock.com

The First Thanksgiving

Read the title. What do you think this text will be about?

Circle the name of the ship that took the Pilgrims to America.

Underline words that tell you:

- what it was like when the Pilgrims got to America.
- the name of the Indian tribe that helped them.
- who brought food to the feast.

My Notes

_____

_____

The Pilgrims were one of the first groups to leave England and come to America. They left England because they wanted more freedom. In 1620, the Pilgrims came to America on the Mayflower. It was cold. There was not much food. It was hard for them to stay alive.

The Wampanoag tribe showed the Pilgrims how to grow food. At the first good harvest, the Pilgrims and American Indians had a feast. Both brought food and celebrated together.

American Indians taught the Pilgrims to grow vegetables like pumpkins and corn. People still eat these foods at Thanksgiving today!

orensila/iStock/Getty Images

The Mayflower is the ship that brought the Pilgrims to America.

2 Find Evidence

Reread Why was it hard for the Pilgrims to stay alive?

Underline the words that show you.

3 Make Connections

Talk How did the American Indians help the Pilgrims?

Explore Key Details

Key details help you understand a text.

To find key details:

1. Read the title. This is what the text is about. Circle the title.

2. Read the whole text.

3. Look for information that helps you understand the text. This is a key detail. Underline it.

 COLLABORATE Work with your class to complete the chart below.

Holiday: Thanksgiving	
Key Detail Pilgrims came to America on the Mayflower.	**Key Detail**

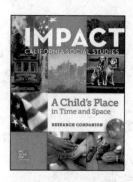

Investigate!

Read pages 130–137 in your Research Companion.

Look for details about holidays in your text.

Write the details in your graphic organizer.

Holiday: Cesar Chavez Day	Holiday: Martin Luther King, Jr. Day	Holiday: Veterans Day	Holiday: Earth Day
Key Detail Chavez helped farm workers.	Key Detail	Key Detail	Key Detail We celebrate our home, the Earth.
Key Detail	Key Detail We can be kind to others.	Key Detail We have parades for the veterans.	Key Detail

Think About It

Think about your research. Why do we celebrate important people?

Write About It

Write an invitation about a holiday. Tell what you are celebrating, why you are celebrating it, and how you will celebrate it.

_____

_____

_____

_____

_____

_____

_____

Talk About It
COLLABORATE

Share your invitation with a partner. Then talk
about how we celebrate the holiday you chose.

Citizenship

Connect to the
ESSENTIAL EQ QUESTION

Take Action

Which holiday do you think is the best celebration of our country?
Use your notes from the graphic organizer to choose a holiday.
Then complete the sentence.

_____ is the best celebration of

America because _____

_____.

ESSENTIAL EQ QUESTION

Inquiry Project Notes

_____

_____

_____

Inquiry Project Wrap Up

Class Big Book of Important Symbols

Now's the time for your team to share your project with the class. Here's what to do.

☐ Pick a few of your favorite symbols from your Big Book. Talk about how these symbols celebrate our country.

☐ Explain what steps you followed to make your Big Book.

☐ Show your Big Book to the class.

Tips for Presenting

Remember these tips when you present to your class.

☐ Describe each symbol and what it means.

☐ Include details about each symbol or picture.

☐ Express your ideas and feelings clearly.

☐ Relax and enjoy yourself!

Project Rubric

Use these questions to help evaluate your project.

	Yes	No
Does each symbol have a picture?		
Is each symbol explained in our Big Book?		
Did people understand what each symbol in our Big Book means?		
Did we work well as a team?		

Project Reflection

Think about the work that you did in this chapter, either with a group or on your own. Describe something that you think you did very well. What would you do differently?

_____

_____

_____

_____

Chapter 4

Past and Present

How Is Our Life Different from the Past, and How Is It the Same?

In this chapter, you'll explore what life was like in the past. You'll read about how it has changed or stayed the same. You'll also work with a team to create a museum display. The display will show how one part of life was different long ago.

COLLABORATE

Talk About It

Discuss with a partner what questions you have about what life was like in the past.

My Research Questions

1._____

_____

2._____

_____

HSS 1.2.1, HSS 1.2.4, HSS 1.4, HSS 1.4.1,
HSS 1.4.2, HSS 1.4.3, HSS 1.5.3,
HSS 1.6.2, HAS.CS.1.1, HAS.CS.1.2,
HAS.CS.1.3, HAS.HR.1.2

Inquiry Project

Displaying the Past

In this project, each team creates a display about one part of life, such as transportation, clothing, or school.

Here's your project checklist.

☐ **Brainstorm** about what part of life you would like to show from the past.

☐ **Collect** images and information about the part of life you chose to show.

☐ **Think** about how this part of life should be displayed. Should you use an artifact? Should you draw a picture or build a sculpture? Does someone in your group have an artifact to bring in and share?

☐ **Make** a museum display. Make sure you include a written explanation of it.

☐ **Present** your museum display. Listen to the other groups. Discuss how parts of life from the past have changed.

Complete this chapter's Word Rater. Write notes as you learn more about each word.

equipment

My Notes

☐ Know It!
☐ Heard It!
☐ Don't Know It!

_____

_____

_____

history

My Notes

☐ Know It!
☐ Heard It!
☐ Don't Know It!

_____

_____

_____

interview

My Notes

☐ Know It!
☐ Heard It!
☐ Don't Know It!

_____

_____

_____

invent (v.)

My Notes

☐ Know It!
☐ Heard It!
☐ Don't Know It!

_____

_____

_____

invention (*n.*) My Notes

☐ Know It! _____

☐ Heard It! _____

☐ Don't Know It! _____

_____

produce (*v.*)   My Notes

☐ Know It! _____

☐ Heard It! _____

☐ Don't Know It! _____

_____

technology   My Notes

☐ Know It! _____

☐ Heard It! _____

☐ Don't Know It! _____

_____

How Can We Discover History?

Lesson Outcomes

What Am I Learning?
You will explore what we can learn from life long ago.

Why Am I Learning It?
You will learn how to explore your own community's past.

How Will I Know that I Learned It?
You will draw events from your own past.

Talk About It

COLLABORATE

Look closely at the picture. What are the people doing? What kind of animal is pulling the wagon? How is this different from the way most people travel today?

HSS 1.4.2, HSS 1.4.3

1 Inspect

Look at the photos.

Underline key details in the text.

Circle words that you don't know.

Take notes on the page. What is one way we learn about the past?

My Notes

_____

_____

_____

_____

_____

Life Long Ago

The past can mean any time before now. It can mean yesterday. It can also mean a long time ago. There are many ways to learn about the past. One way is to look at photos taken long ago.

Long ago, some people built sod houses. Sod bricks are made from grass, roots, and dirt.

Prints and Photographs Division, Library of Congress, LC-DIG-ppmsca-08377

Old photos can tell you a lot about the past. Look at all the details in the photos. Think about life now. What was different in the past?

This photo was taken long ago. Some toys are different today than they were in the past. Some toys are the same.

2 Find Evidence

Look Again How do the photos help you understand life long ago?

Discuss Look at the girls' clothes. How are clothes different now?

3 Make Connections

Talk Talk about life long ago. COLLABORATE What is the same about life in the past and life today? What is different?

Turn back to page 155. How is the photo on this page like the photo on page 155?

Explore Key Details

A **key detail** tells you important information about the main topic.

The **main topic** is what a text is about.

1. Look for key details in the text.

2. Look for key details in photos and charts.

 COLLABORATE Work with your class to complete the graphic organizer.

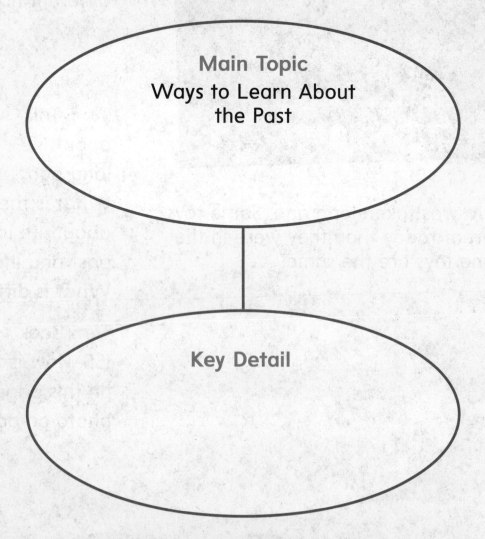

Main Topic
Ways to Learn About
the Past

Key Detail

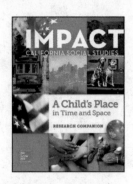

Investigate!

Read pages 148–155 in your Research Companion.

Look for key details related to the main topic.

Write the key details in the graphic organizer below.

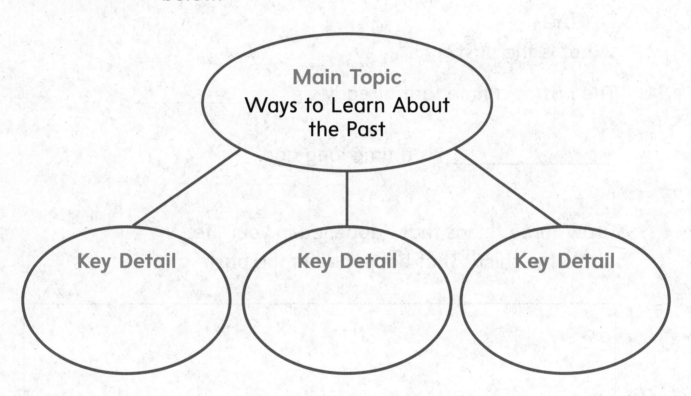

Main Topic
Ways to Learn About the Past

Key Detail

Key Detail

Key Detail

Think About It

Think about what you have learned. What is the past?
How do we learn about it?

Write About It

Define

What is the past?

The past is a time that already _____ .

_____ is a time long ago.

Draw It

Draw three things that happened in your life.
Circle the things that happened in the past.

Talk About It

COLLABORATE

Explain

Share your drawings with a partner.
What important events did you include?

History

Connect to the EQ

ESSENTIAL QUESTION

Take Action

Imagine you want to learn about your community
in the past. What would you do to find out about it?
Where would you go? Who would you ask?

I. _____

_____

2. _____

_____

3. _____

_____

Lesson 2

How Has School Changed?

Lesson Outcomes

What Am I Learning?
You will explore what schools were like long ago.

Why Am I Learning It?
You will understand how school has changed.

How Will I Know that I Learned It?
You will be able to tell how schools today and long ago are the same and different.

Talk About It COLLABORATE

Look at the picture. What shows that this picture is from the present and not the past?

HSS 1.2.1, HSS 1.4, HSS 1.4.1

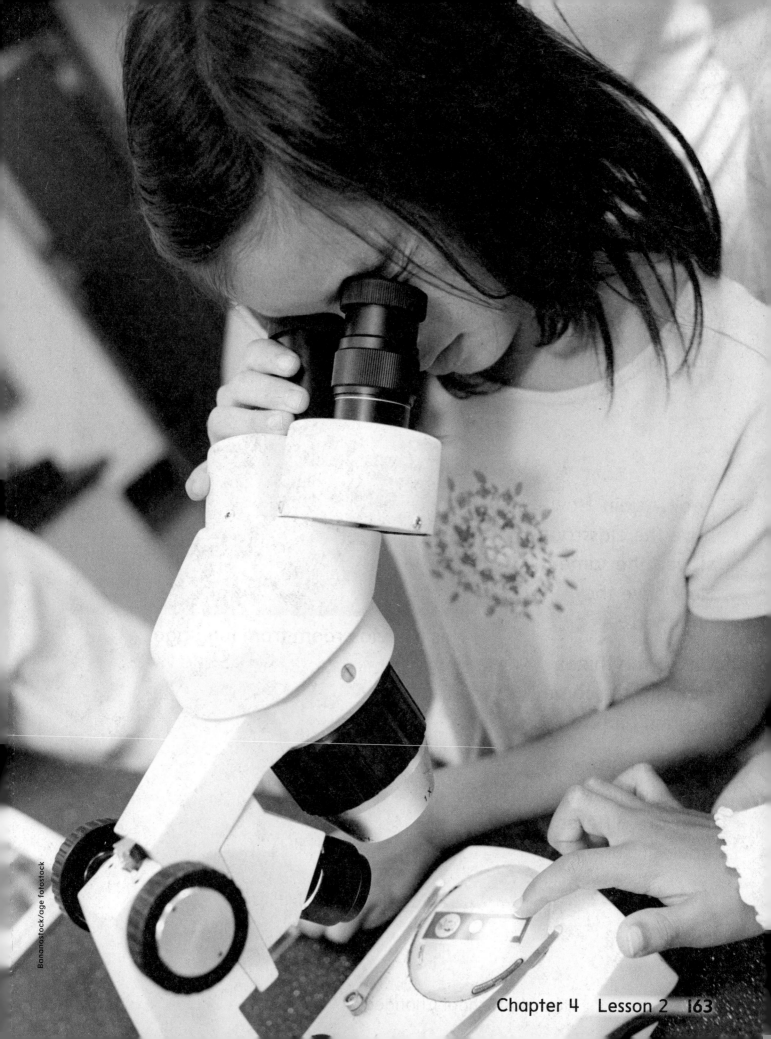

1 Inspect

Look closely at the photos.

Take notes on the page. Write down questions you have about the photos.

2 Find Evidence

Look Again How have the classrooms stayed the same? How have they changed?

Circle the things that are the same in each picture.

Draw an arrow to point to the things that are different in each picture.

This is a classroom from long ago.

Prints and Photographs Division, Library of Congress, LC-USZ62-112557

This is a classroom today.

3 Make Connections

Write What would you ask the students from long ago? Write one question.

Explore Compare and Contrast

When you **compare** two things, you think about how they are alike.

When you **contrast** two things, you think about how they are different.

To compare and contrast:

1. Study the two pictures.

2. Look for things that are alike.

3. Now look for things that are different.

 COLLABORATE Work with your class to complete the graphic organizer.

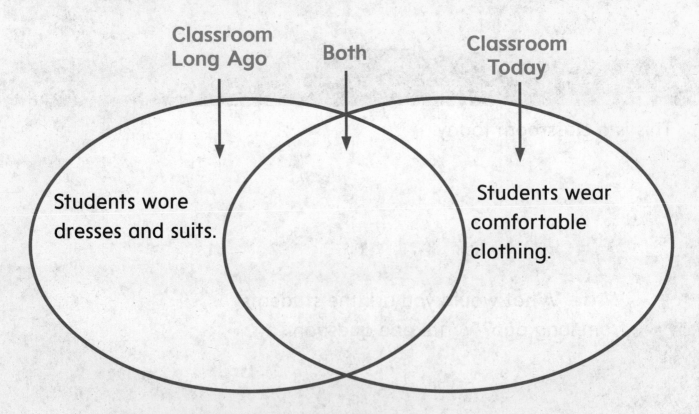

Classroom Long Ago   Both   Classroom Today

Students wore dresses and suits.

Students wear comfortable clothing.

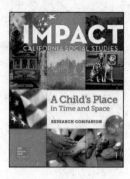

Investigate!

Read pages 156-163 in your Research Companion.

Look for details about how schools long ago and today are the same and different.

Write your information in the graphic organizer.

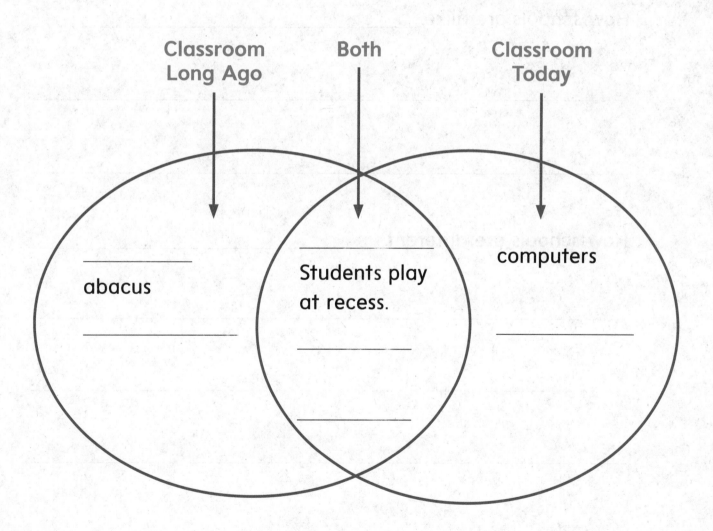

Classroom Long Ago   Both   Classroom Today

_____

abacus

_____

Students play at recess.

_____

_____

computers

_____

Think About It

Think about what you read. How is school
the same as it was long ago? How is it different?

Write About It

Write one sentence to tell how schools are alike.
Write one sentence to tell how they are different.

How schools are alike: _____

_____

_____

How schools are different: _____

_____

_____

_____

Talk About It

Explain

Share your sentences with a partner.

Discuss why schools are better now than in the past.

Connect to the EQ

Imagine it is the first day of school long ago. With a partner, make a list of all the school supplies you would need.

Then, make a list of supplies you need as a student today.

School Supplies	
Then	Now

Lesson Outcomes

What Am I Learning?

You will explore how transportation has changed over time.

Why Am I Learning It?

You will write about different ways that people travel and use transportation.

How Will I Know that I Learned It?

You will explain which changes in transportation affected people's lives the most.

Talk About It

Look closely at the picture. Does this ship look old or new? Do you think people travel on ships like this today? Why or why not?

NEW YORK CLIPPER SHIP "CHALLENGE".

Read the title. What do you think this text will be about?

Circle words you don't know.

Underline clues that tell you:

- how people got to places in the past.
- how people get to places today.

My Notes

_____

_____

_____

_____

What Is Transportation?

A way of moving people and things from place to place is called transportation. In the past, people mostly walked or rode horses. It took a long time for people to get places.

Later, people made wagons. These trips were faster. But they were still long and hard. Some trips took weeks or even months!

People used wagons long ago.

Prints and Photographs Division, Library of Congress, LC-USZ62-108279

People drive big trucks today.

©Henryk Sadura/Alamy Stock Photo

People made new **inventions** for travel. Inventions are new things that help people. Today, it is easy to get places. People can drive cars or trucks. They can take fast trains. They can fly on planes. Trips may take only a few hours.

2 Find Evidence

Reread Is transportation better today? Why or why not?

Underline words that show what you think.

3 Make Connections

Draw
Draw a picture of transportation in the past and transportation today.

Explore Sequence

Authors sometimes give information in **sequence**, or time order. Words like *first, later,* and *today* can help you understand sequence.

To understand sequence:

1. Read the text all the way through. Look for words like *first, later,* and *today*.

2. Find what happened first. Circle it.

3. Find what happened later. Underline it.

4. Find what happens today. Highlight it.

 COLLABORATE   Work with your class to complete the graphic organizer.

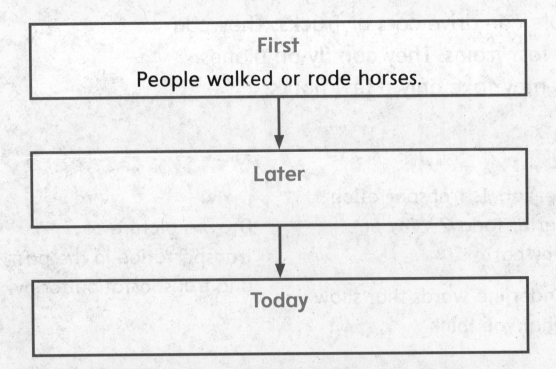

First
People walked or rode horses.

Later

Today

Investigate!

Read pages 164–173 in your Research Companion.

Look for key details about what happened first and later, and what happens today.

Write your information in the graphic organizer.

First

Cars: cost a lot of money

Planes: flew for only a few seconds

↓

Later

Cars: _____

Planes: _____

↓

Today

Cars: _____

Planes: _____

Think About It

Think about what you have read.
How has transportation changed?

Write About It

List three different kinds of transportation:

1. _____

2. _____

3. _____

Talk About It

COLLABORATE

Explain

Share your list with a partner. Talk about how transportation has changed.

Connect to the EQ

History

ESSENTIAL EQ QUESTION

What kind of transportation changed people's lives the most? Tell why you think so.

_____

_____

_____

ESSENTIAL EQ QUESTION

Inquiry Project Notes

_____

_____

_____

How Has Work Changed?

Lesson Outcomes

What Am I Learning?
You will learn about work in the past and work today.

Why Am I Learning It?
You will talk and write about how and why work has changed over time.

How Will I Know that I Learned It?
You will write about one job and how it was different in the past and what it is like today.

Talk About It

Look closely at the photo. What are the people doing?

What details in the photo help you learn about farming long ago?

1 Inspect

Read Look at the title. What do you think this text will be about?

Underline words that tell how farmers did their work long ago.

Circle words that you don't understand.

My Notes

_____

_____

_____

_____

Farming Then and Now

Long ago, most of the people in the United States lived on farms. They **produced** their own food. They grew or raised it on their land. Farmers sold or traded food that was left over. Family farms were small.

Farmers did work by hand or with horse-drawn **equipment**, or tools. They worked hard. They worked every day.

Today, most farms produce food for others to eat. Farmers use machines instead of horses. This equipment is faster. It makes work easier. Farmers can grow more crops. They can raise more animals.

One thing is the same about farming long ago and today. Farm families work hard!

A "combine" machine helps to gather wheat on a California farm.

2 Find Evidence

Reread What do the text and the photo tell you about farm equipment?

Underline the words that tell what farmers can do with new equipment.

3 Make Connections

Talk Why is modern farm equipment faster than horse-drawn equipment?

Glow Images

Explore Make Connections

Making connections means that text and pictures work together. They both show clues that can tell you about an important idea.

To make connections:

1. Read the text. Underline details that tell more about the important idea.

2. Look at the picture. Circle the parts of the picture that show clues about the idea.

3. Make connections between the text, the picture, and the idea.

 COLLABORATE Work with your class to complete the graphic organizer.

Text Details	Picture Clues	Idea
Farmers grew or raised their own food.		Long ago, families had to work together on farms.

Investigate!

Read pages 174-181 in your Research Companion.

Look for details in the text and pictures.

Write your information in the graphic organizer.

Text Details	Picture Clues	Idea
In the past, workers used equipment like _____ _____ _____ to get jobs done. Today, workers use equipment like _____ _____ _____ to get jobs done.	In the past, firefighters used _____ _____ _____. Today, they use _____. Workers today use _____ _____ to get jobs done.	In the past, workers did not have _____ _____. Today, machines and computers make work _____ _____ _____.

Think About It

Think about what you read. What is one way work has changed over time?

Write About It

Think about a job you might like to have when you grow up. What is one way this job might have been different in the past?

When I grow up, I would like to _____

_____

_____

_____ .

In the past, this job might have been _____

because _____

_____

_____ .

Talk About It

Explain

Share your job with a partner. Tell your partner what
your job was like in the past. Tell what it is like today.

 History

Connect to the ESSENTIAL EQ QUESTION

A Day in the Life

Choose a job you learned about. Write a dialogue between two
characters that have that job. One character has the job in the
past, and one has the job today. Have your characters tell each
other how they work and what it is like to do that job.

_____

_____

_____

_____

_____

How Has Daily Life Changed?

Lesson Outcomes

What Am I Learning?
You will explore how daily life has changed over time.

Why Am I Learning It?
You will be able to describe how daily life was different in the past.

How Will I Know that I Learned It?
You will form an opinion about whether daily life is better now or in the past.

Talk About It

Look closely at the picture of the kitchen. Is this the kind of kitchen people use today or used in the past? What details make you think so?

Cooking Then and Now

Kitchens from 200 years ago were very different. They had no stoves, sinks, or refrigerators. People cooked their food over a wood fire. They had no running water or electricity. They didn't even have simple tools like apple peelers! Many people dried their food and stored it in jars and sacks.

Over time, people made new tools. This changed the way people cooked. One new tool was a heavy stove made of metal. It was called the cast-iron stove. It made cooking much faster. People could boil water and bake a cake at the same time. Then the refrigerator was invented. People could store frozen food. They could save leftovers. Today, new tools make cooking easier. A microwave oven can cook food in seconds!

Kitchens today have stoves and refrigerators.

2 Find Evidence

Reread Think about how new tools in the kitchen affected people's daily lives. What could people do that they could not do before? What tool made it easier to store food?

Underline clues that support what you think.

3 Make Connections

Talk How has cooking changed over time?

What inventions led to these changes?

Explore Ask and Answer Questions

When you read, you can **ask questions** about the text. You can ask about things you don't understand.

COLLABORATE   Work with your class to complete the graphic organizer.

Question	Answer
How were kitchens in the past different from today?	
What new tools do people have in kitchens today?	
	They dried their food and stored it in jars and sacks.

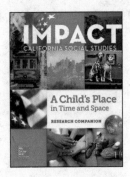

Investigate!

Read pages 182-189 in your Research Companion.

Look for evidence that helps you compare and contrast life then and now.

Write your information in the graphic organizer.

Question	Answer

Think About It

Based on what you read, how is our daily life different from daily life in the past?

Write About It

Choose one part of daily life that was different in the past. Draw a picture of it. Add labels to explain your drawing.

Talk About It

COLLABORATE

Tell your partner about your drawing. Can your partner tell you how that part of life has changed?

Connect to the EQ

ESSENTIAL QUESTION

History

Do you think daily life is better now or long ago? Tell why you think so.

_____

_____

_____

_____

_____

_____

Inquiry Project Wrap Up

Displaying the Past

Now's the time for your team to share your project. Here's what to do.

☐ Tell what part of life from the past your museum display shows.

☐ Explain how you made your display. Tell people what steps you followed.

☐ Talk about how well you think it worked.

☐ Show your museum display to the class.

Tips for Presenting

Remember these tips when you present to your class.

☐ Speak loudly and clearly.

☐ Describe what your display shows.

☐ Explain why your display helps tell about the past.

☐ Answer any questions your classmates might have.

Project Rubric

Use these questions to help evaluate your project.

	Yes	No
Does our display show a part of life from the past?		
Is our display explained in writing?		
Do people understand what part of life from the past our display is showing?		
Did we work well as a team?		

Project Reflection

Think about the work that you did in this chapter, either with a group or own your own. Describe something that you think you did very well. What would you do differently?

_____

_____

_____

_____

Chapter 5 — People of America

ESSENTIAL EQ QUESTION

How Do Many Different People Make One Nation?

In this chapter, you'll explore how one nation can be made of many people. You'll read about some of the places Americans come from, and some of the things they bring with them. You'll also work with a team on a chapter project to make a drama, or play, out of a folktale.

Talk About It COLLABORATE

Discuss with a partner what questions you have about how one nation can be made of many people. Write your questions.

My Research Questions

1. _____

_____

2. _____

_____

HSS 1.1.2, HSS 1.2.4, HSS 1.4.1, HSS 1.4.3,
HSS 1.5, HSS 1.5.1, HSS 1.5.2,
HSS 1.5.3, HAS.CS.1.3, HAS.CS.1.4,
HAS.HR.1.2, HAS.HR.1.3, HAS.HI.1.2

Inquiry Project

Important Stories

In this project, you'll work with a team to make a drama, or play. With your group, choose one of the folktales from Lesson 2.

Here's your project checklist.

☐ **Summarize** the story. Think of how you could act out what happens in the story.

☐ **Assign roles** to each member of your group. Be sure to include everyone. You could even write new people into the stories to give everyone a role.

☐ **Think** about what the story is about. How can you best tell what the story is about in a drama, or play?

☐ **Rehearse** the scenes from the drama that you have written. Make sure everyone is involved.

☐ **Present** your drama. Watch the other groups as they present their dramas.

Explore Words

Complete this chapter's Word Rater. Write notes as you learn more about each word.

culture

My Notes

☐ Know It!

☐ Heard It!

☐ Don't Know It!

_____

_____

_____

custom

My Notes

☐ Know It!

☐ Heard It!

☐ Don't Know It!

_____

_____

_____

immigrant

My Notes

☐ Know It!

☐ Heard It!

☐ Don't Know It!

_____

_____

_____

tradition

My Notes

☐ Know It!

☐ Heard It! _____

☐ Don't Know It! _____

_____

tribe

My Notes

☐ Know It!

☐ Heard It! _____

☐ Don't Know It! _____

_____

Lesson Outcomes

What Am I Learning?
You will learn about different cultures around the world.

Why Am I Learning It?
You will be able to explain how cultures are alike and different.

How Will I Know that I Learned It?
You will write about different cultures in the United States.

Talk About It

Look closely at the picture. What are the people doing?

What do you think the artist is trying to say? Tell why you think so.

HSS 1.5.1, HSS 1.5.3

1 Inspect

Read Look at the title. What do you think this text will be about?

Circle words you don't know.

Underline clues that tell you:

- something all people do.
- what kind of food many people eat.
- where different foods come from.

My Notes

_____

_____

_____

_____

Let's Eat!

People around the world do many of the same things, like eat and work and play. They also do some things differently. The special ways that people do things is called **culture**.

Part of culture is the way we eat. Families from different cultures cook and eat different types of food. They often eat the foods they know well.

Around the world, people share meals with their family and friends. Cooking and sharing food is one way that friends get to know each other. This is one way that people are very much the same.

Rolls, loaves, buns – there are all kinds of breads! Many foods in the United States, like types of bread, come from cultures around the world.

Pita bread is soft, flat bread. People eat pita bread in Greece and other countries. Tortillas are another type of bread. Some tortillas are made from corn. Tortillas are popular in Mexico and around the world. What is your favorite kind of bread?

Dinner can be a time for families to talk and eat.

2 Find Evidence

Reread What do you think might be the same in many cultures?

Underline clues that tell you:

- one way people get to know each other.
- who people share meals with around the world.

Discuss What kinds of food do you like to share with your friends?

3 Make Connections

Talk What kinds of food do you know from cultures around the world?

COLLABORATE

Explore Summarizing

A **summary** is a short way to explain what you read.

To summarize:

1. Read the whole text. Look for important details.

2. Decide which details are important.

3. Tell all the important details in your own words.

 COLLABORATE Work with your class to complete the graphic organizer.

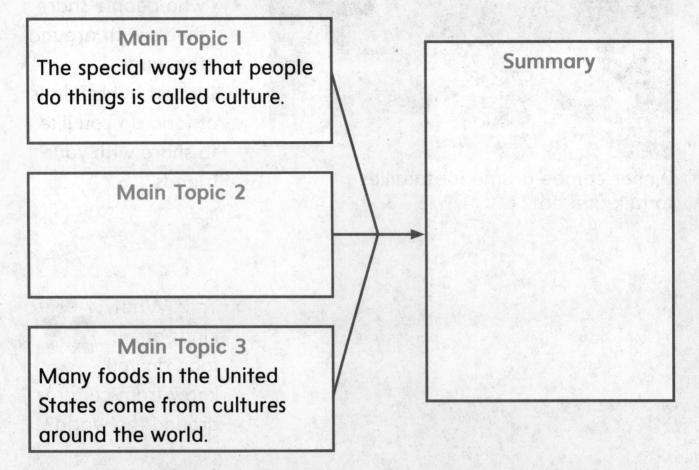

Main Topic 1
The special ways that people do things is called culture.

Main Topic 2

Main Topic 3
Many foods in the United States come from cultures around the world.

Summary

Investigate!

Read pages 200–205 in your Research Companion.

Look for the main ideas.

Write your notes to summarize the main ideas of what you read.

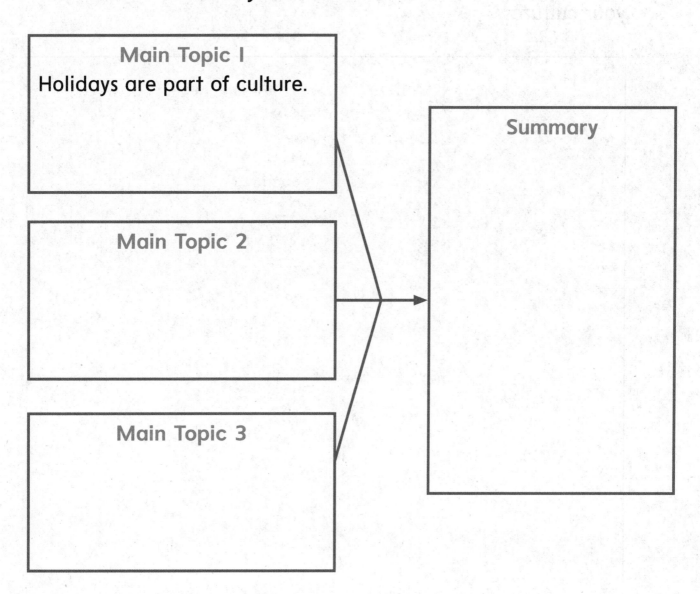

Main Topic 1

Holidays are part of culture.

Main Topic 2

Main Topic 3

Summary

Think About It

Think about what you have read. What is culture?

Draw It

Draw and label a picture that shows something from your culture.

Talk About It

COLLABORATE

Explain

Share your picture with a partner. Explain your ideas, and answer your partner's questions about your drawing.

🏛 Connect to the ESSENTIAL EQ QUESTION
Civics

What parts of different cultures can you find in the United States? Give examples based on what you know and what you read.

I. We eat foods _____

_____

2. Our holidays _____

_____

3. We listen to _____

ESSENTIAL EQ QUESTION   Inquiry Project Notes

_____

_____

What Can We Learn About Culture from Literature?

Lesson Outcomes

What Am I Learning?
You will explore the stories people tell and what they say about cultures.

Why Am I Learning It?
You will understand what favorite stories say about cultures.

How Will I Know that I Learned It?
You will explain how you share your culture through the stories you tell.

Talk About It COLLABORATE

Look at the picture. What is the woman doing? How can you tell?

HSS 1.5.1, HSS 1.5.3

1 Inspect

Read Look at the title. What do you think this lesson will be about?

Circle words you don't know.

Underline clues that tell you:

- what we can learn from stories.
- what characters can do.

Take notes on the page.

My Notes

_____

_____

_____

We Share Stories

People around the world share stories. Sometimes these stories help us understand what the world is like. The characters can show what is important in American culture.

Some stories are about pretend heroes. Paul Bunyan is a folk hero. He was a big, hard-working lumberjack. Paul Bunyan shows how to be brave and strong.

Other stories are about real people, like Paul Revere. He warned Americans that enemy troops were coming during a war. Paul Revere had a secret plan to help his people. He showed how to be clever and caring.

Every culture has stories to share.

2 Find Evidence

Reread What does the picture tell you about storytelling?

Underline things that are important in American culture.

3 Make Connections

Talk Why do we tell stories about heroes? Who are some of your heroes?

COLLABORATE

Explore Compare and Contrast

When you **compare** two things, you see how they are alike.

When you **contrast** two things, you see how they are different.

COLLABORATE Work with your class to complete the graphic organizer below.

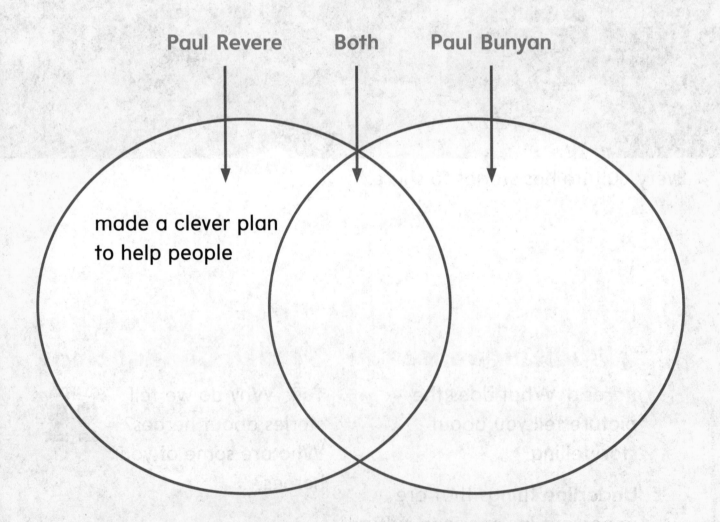

Paul Revere   Both   Paul Bunyan

made a clever plan
to help people

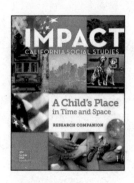

Investigate!

Read pages 206–213 in your Research Companion.

Look for details about the girls in the two stories.

Write the details in your graphic organizer.

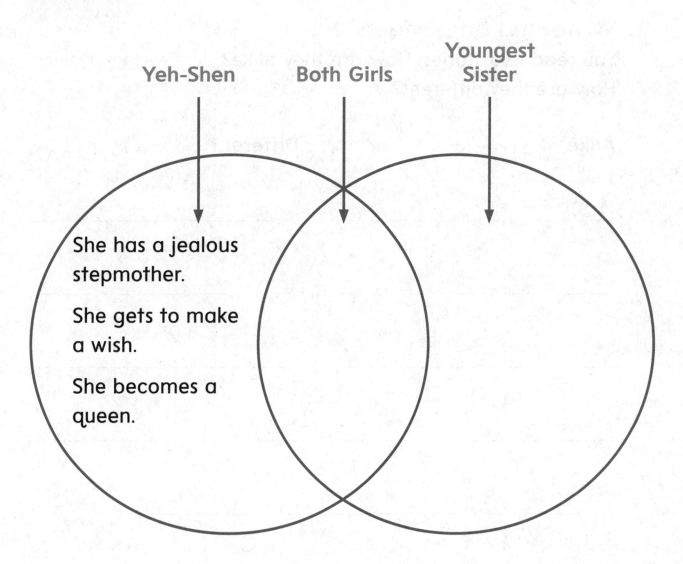

Yeh-Shen   Both Girls   Youngest Sister

She has a jealous stepmother.

She gets to make a wish.

She becomes a queen.

Think About It

Think about what you read. What do stories and poems tell about culture?

Write About It

Write and Cite Evidence

You read two stories. How are they alike? How are they different?

Alike	Different
_____	_____
_____	_____
_____	_____
_____	_____
_____	_____
_____	_____

Talk About It

COLLABORATE

Explain

Share your answers with your partner. Why do you
think the stories are different?

 **Connect to the**

Civics

ESSENTIAL EQ QUESTION

Why do you think we read stories from different cultures?
Think about what you learned from the stories you read.

_____

_____

_____

_____

_____

_____

What Are Customs?

Lesson Outcomes

What Am I Learning?
You will learn about different customs.

Why Am I Learning It?
You will be able to tell what customs are and describe some customs.

How Will I Know that I Learned It?
You will tell about different customs in your family and community.

Talk About It

Look at the picture and the map. What are the people doing? Where do they live?

HSS 1.5.1, HSS 1.5.3

Top Photo Corporation/Getty Images

Analyze the Source

1 Inspect

Look at the picture and title. What do you think you will learn?

Read the text.

Circle words you don't know.

Underline clues that tell you what the people are doing.

Take notes on the page.

My Notes

_____

_____

_____

_____

Celebrate!

Customs are things that a group of people do. Every culture has special customs. One kind of custom is when people celebrate. People celebrate important events, like family reunions or the New Year. Celebrations are fun!

Some people from Latin countries celebrate with a Quinceañera. Say it like this: *Kin-sin-nyair-a*. It is a birthday party for a 15-year-old girl. Families bring special kinds of food. They dance to music and eat a special cake.

Other celebrations include:

- a wedding
- a graduation ceremony
- a baby shower

A family celebrates the girl's Quinceañera with a party. A Quinceañera is a custom that comes from Mexico and other Latin countries.

Where in the World?

Mexico

2 Find Evidence

Talk Why do people have a Quinceañera?

3 Make Connections

Talk The word *Quinceañera* comes from the Spanish words for "15" and "years." What does this tell you about the celebration?

COLLABORATE

Explore Compare and Contrast

When you **compare**, you show how things are alike.

When you **contrast**, you show how they are different.

To compare and contrast:

1. Read the whole text. It is about celebrations.

2. Think about two celebrations. How are they the same?

3. Then think about how they are different.

COLLABORATE Work with your class to complete the graphic organizer below.

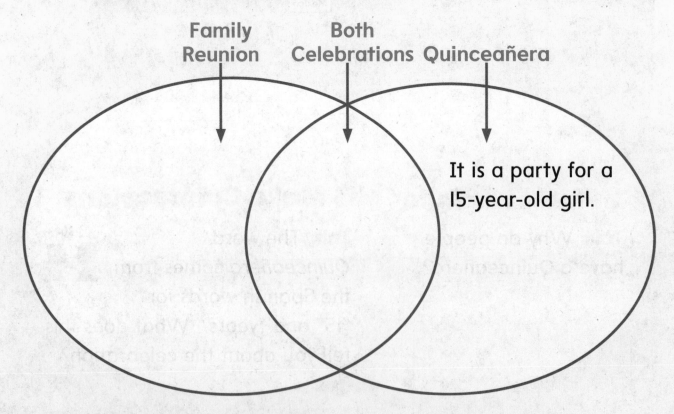

Family Reunion   Both Celebrations   Quinceañera

It is a party for a 15-year-old girl.

Investigate!

Read pages 214–219 in your Research Companion.

Look for details about the Chinese New Year and the Persian New Year. How are they alike and different?

Write your information in the graphic organizer.

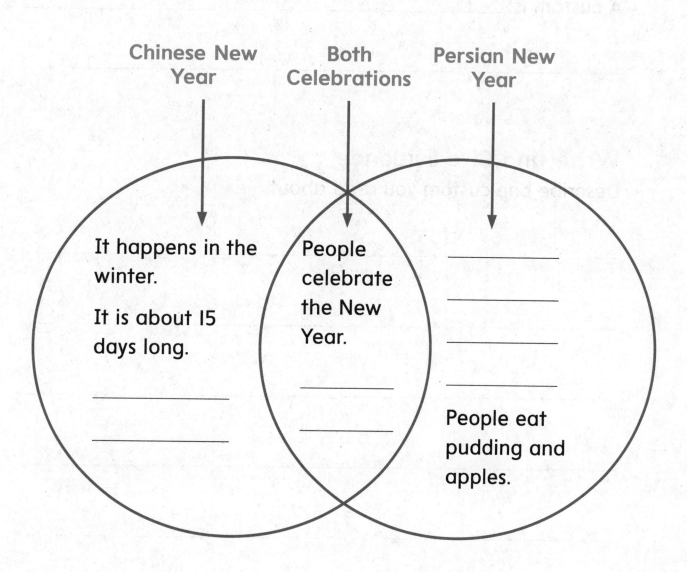

Chinese New Year

Both Celebrations

Persian New Year

It happens in the winter.

It is about 15 days long.

_____

_____

People celebrate the New Year.

_____

_____

_____

_____

_____

_____

People eat pudding and apples.

Think About It

Think about what you read. What are customs?

Write About It

Define

What is a custom?

A custom is _____

_____.

Write and Cite Evidence

Describe one custom you read about.

_____

_____

_____

_____

_____

Talk About It

Explain

Share your answers with a partner. What details can you add?

Connect to the

History

Take Action

Tell about three ways people in your community celebrate their customs.

1. Some people _____

_____.

2. Some people _____

_____.

3. Some people _____

_____.

Who First Lived in North America?

Lesson Outcomes

What Am I Learning?

You will explore who first lived in North America.

Why Am I Learning It?

You will be able to describe the lives of American Indians.

How Will I Know that I Learned It?

You will explain why learning about American Indian groups is important.

Talk About It   COLLABORATE

Look closely at the picture. What are the people doing?

How are they celebrating the past?

HSS 1.5.2, HSS 1.5.3, HAS.CS.2, HAS.CS.3, HAS.HI.2

1 Inspect

Read the text. Who were the first people to live in North America?

Circle words you don't know.

Underline clues that tell you:

- what North America is.
- how long American Indians have lived in North America.

Take notes on the page.

My Notes

_____

_____

_____

American Indians in North America

North America is a continent. Canada, the United States, and Mexico are part of North America. American Indians were the first people to live in North America. They are also called Native Americans. They have lived here for more than 10,000 years!

There are many American Indian groups. These groups are called **tribes**. Each tribe is different. People in each tribe share the same language, customs, and beliefs.

American Indians teach families about their culture.

2 Find Evidence

Compare How are the people in a tribe alike?

Underline the words that tell how people in a tribe are alike.

3 Make Connections

Talk Look back at the text. How are tribes different?

COLLABORATE

Explore Main Topic and Key Details

The **main topic** is what the selection is about.
Key details tell information about the topic.

Words and photos can tell about the main topic and key details.

To find the main topic and key details:

1. Read the whole text.

2. Circle the main topic.

3. Look for information about the main topic in the text and the pictures. Underline the key details.

 COLLABORATE Work with your class to complete the graphic organizer below.

Main Topic
American Indians were the first people to live in North America.

Key Detail	Key Detail	Key Detail
	There are many American Indian groups.	

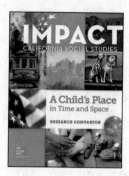

Investigate!

Read pages 220–225 in your Research Companion.

Look for the main topic and key details.

Write your information in the graphic organizer.

Main Topic
American Indian stories, traditions, and history can teach lessons.

Key Detail	Key Detail	Key Detail
On Native American Day, people can learn how tribes lived in the past and how they live today.		

Think About It

What is one part of American Indian culture?

Write About It

List two things you learned about American Indians.

1. _____

_____

_____

_____

2. _____

_____

_____

_____

Talk About It

COLLABORATE

Explain

Share what you learned with a partner.
What did your partner learn?

Civics

Connect to the EQ

ESSENTIAL QUESTION

Make Connections

Why do you think it is important to learn about the people
who first lived in North America? Think about details you
learned about American Indian culture as you write.

_____

_____

_____

_____

_____

_____

What Did Immigrants Bring to the United States?

Lesson Outcomes

What Am I Learning?

You will learn why immigrants came to the United States and what they brought with them.

Why Am I Learning It?

You will understand how immigrants helped make America what it is today.

How Will I Know that I Learned It?

You will tell about what immigrants brought to the United States.

Talk About It

COLLABORATE

Look at the picture and read the caption. Why do you think these people came to the United States?

HSS 1.5.2

232 Lesson 5 What Did Immigrants Bring to the United States?

Everett Historical/Shutterstock.com

The people in this picture have just arrived in the United States. They came from another country.

1 Inspect

Read the title. What do you think this text will be about?

Circle the words that you do not know.

Underline words that tell you:

- who immigrants are.
- what immigrants bring to America.

Take notes on the page.

My Notes

_____

_____

_____

People Come to America

Immigrants are people who come to one country from another. Many want a better life. Some come to work. Immigrants bring skills to the United States.

People bring other things too, like food and sports. They also bring their ideas. The cultures of immigrants become part of American culture.

Immigrants look at the Statue of Liberty.

2 Find Evidence

Reread Why does the United States have many different cultures?

3 Make Connections

Talk Why do immigrants move from one country to another country?

COLLABORATE

Explore Cause and Effect

The **effect** is what happened.

The **cause** is why it happened.

To find the cause and effect:

1. Read the whole text.

2. Look for something that happened. This is the effect. Circle it.

3. Look for a detail that tells you why the effect happened. This is the cause. Underline it.

4. Ask yourself, *Did the event cause what happened?*

 COLLABORATE Work with your class to fill in the graphic organizer.

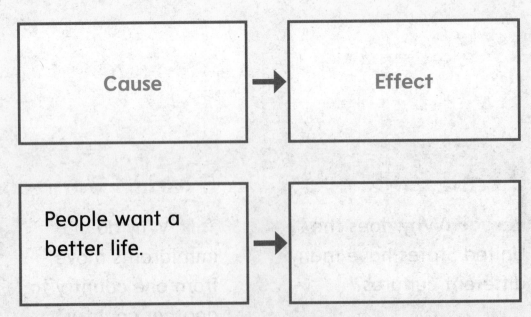

| Cause | → | Effect |

| People want a better life. | → | |

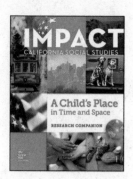

Investigate!

Read pages 226–233 in your Research Companion.

Look for details that tell you what happened and why it happened.

Write the details in your graphic organizer.

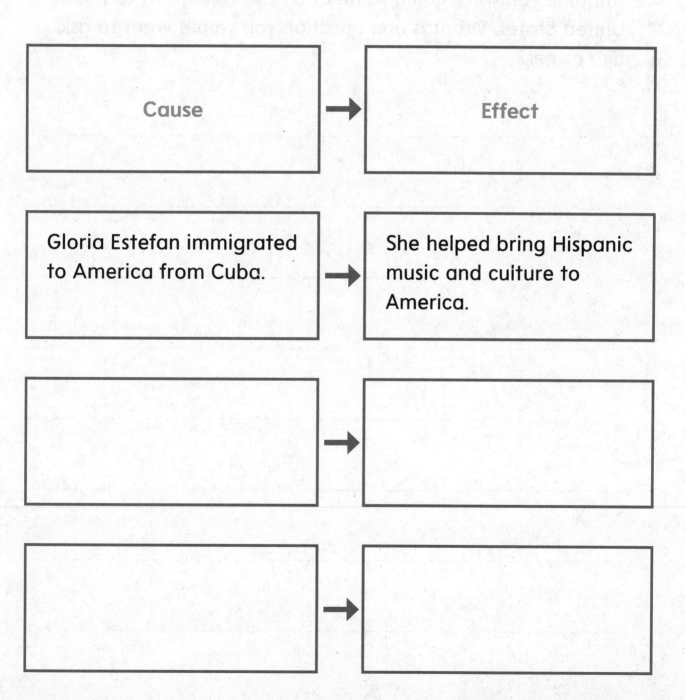

Cause		Effect
	→	
Gloria Estefan immigrated to America from Cuba.	→	She helped bring Hispanic music and culture to America.
	→	
	→	

Think About It

Based on what you read, what did immigrants bring to the United States?

Write About It

Imagine you were going to meet a new immigrant to the United States. What is one question you would want to ask him or her?

_____

_____

_____

_____

_____

_____

_____

Talk About It

COLLABORATE

Share your question with a partner. How do you think an immigrant might answer?

History **Connect to the**

ESSENTIAL EQ QUESTION

Draw a picture of one thing immigrants have added to the culture of the United States.

How Do Traditions Bring Us Together?

Lesson Outcomes

What Am I Learning?
You will learn what traditions are and how they bring people together.

Why Am I Learning It?
You will understand how traditions bring your family or community together.

How Will I Know that I Learned It?
You will write about traditions in your family and community.

Talk About It

COLLABORATE

Look closely at the photo. When was this photo taken? Do you have a dinner like this in your own family or community?

HSS 1.1.2, HSS 1.5.1

PRIMARY SOURCE

Marjory Collins was a photographer
and writer. She took this photo. It
shows people enjoying a special dinner.
This dinner is a tradition.

Traditions We Share

Read the title. What do you think this text will be about?

Circle words you don't know.

Underline clues that will help you answer:

- What is a tradition?
- What is an example of a tradition?
- Why are traditions important?

Take notes on the page.

My Notes

A **tradition** is a way of doing something. It is handed down over the years. The photo of people eating a Thanksgiving meal shows a tradition. People have Thanksgiving dinner every year at the same time of year.

Another tradition in some places is the Pledge of Allegiance. We put our hands on our hearts. Next, we look at the American flag. Then we say the words of the pledge. In many schools, children say the pledge every single morning.

Traditions bring us together. They help us feel like part of a group. We may come from different places. We may have different ways. Traditions are something we can all share.

In some schools, students begin their day by saying the Pledge of Allegiance.

2 Find Evidence

Reread How do the text and photo show us that traditions bring different people together?

Circle clues in the text and photo that support what you think.

3 Make Connections

Talk Why do you think people enjoy traditions?

COLLABORATE

Explore Author's Purpose

The **author's purpose** is the reason why the author writes a text.

To find an author's purpose:

1. Read the text carefully.

2. Look for details that show why the author may have written the text. Details are clues to an author's purpose.

3. Ask yourself, *Why did the author write the text?*

 COLLABORATE

Work with your class to complete the graphic organizer.

Detail
A tradition is a way of doing something that is handed down over the years.

↓

Author's Purpose

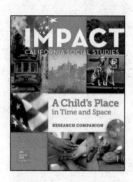

Investigate!

Read pages 234–239 in your Research Companion.

Look for details that help you understand the author's purpose.

Write the details in your graphic organizer.

Details
People can have differences but can share some things too.

↓

Author's Purpose

Think About It

Think about what you read. What kinds of traditions do people share?

_____

_____

Write About It

List three traditions in your family or community.

1. _____

_____

2. _____

_____

3. _____

_____

Talk About It

Explain

Share your list with your partner. How are your lists the same? How are they different?

_{Citizenship} Connect to the EQ

Take Action

What did you learn about your partner's traditions? Write what you learned and what you would like to know more about.

I learned _____

_____

_____

I would like to know more about _____

_____

_____

Inquiry Project Wrap Up

Important Stories

Now's the time for your team to share your project. Here's what to do.

☐ Make sure everyone knows what they are doing in the drama. Rehearse the scene one more time if you need to.

☐ Describe how you made the folktale into a drama, or play.

☐ Talk about how well you think it worked.

☐ Present your drama to the class.

Tips for Performing

Remember these tips when you perform for your class.

☐ Rehearse your drama.

☐ Pretend that you are the character in the drama.

☐ Speak one at a time.

☐ Relax and enjoy yourself!

Project Rubric

Use these questions to help evaluate your project.

	Yes	No
Does our drama tell all the parts in the folktale?		
Do the lines in the drama sound the way that the characters would speak?		
Did we give everyone a role to play in the drama?		
Did people understand the story when we performed it?		
Did we work well as a team?		

Project Reflection

Think about the work that you did in this chapter, either with a group or on your own. Describe something that you think you did very well. What would you do differently?

_____

_____

_____

Welcome to the Neighborhood!

CHARACTERS

Alec, from Greece   **Camila**, from Puerto Rico

Luca, from Italy   **Dora's Papa**

Dora, from Poland   **Narrator**

Narrator: It is the year 1915. Many people have immigrated to New York City. Dora is from Poland. Her family owns a fruit stand.

Dora's Papa: I need to go to the shoemaker. Mind the fruit stand, ok Dora? *(Dora's Papa leaves.)*

Dora: I sure wish I wasn't working. I want to play stickball! *(Alec and Luca walk up.)*

Luca: Did someone say stickball?

Alec: We'll play with you, Dora!

Dora: I can't play. I have to mind the fruit stand.
Besides, we need another person to play.

Luca: Can't you take a little break?

(Camila walks by. She looks shy and a little scared.)

Alec: Hey, maybe she can play.

Dora: I've never seen her before. She must be new.

Luca: Hey, you! You want to play stickball with us?

Camila: Sorry, I don't know much English. I'm from Puerto Rico.
I'm new here.

Alec: That's ok. We're all from someplace else. Luca's family is from Italy. Dora's family is from Poland. And I'm from Greece.

Dora: Do you want to play stickball?

Camila: What is stickball? I don't know American customs.

Alec: We can teach you! Then you can teach us something new.

Camila: I can show you how to cook plantains. It is a kind of fruit. What kind of food do you eat?

Alec: My mother makes pita. It is bread that is flat.

Luca: My father makes meatballs just like they do in Italy.

Dora: We make potato pancakes for special holidays.

Camila: Wow! That sounds good!

(Dora's Papa comes back.)

Dora's Papa: Hello. You must be with the new family down the street.

Camila: Yes, my name is Camila.

Dora: Camila eats a kind of fruit I never heard of. They are called plantains.

Dora's Papa: Hmm. Maybe we should sell them at the fruit stand.

Dora: And then we can sell them to Camila's family.

Dora's Papa: That's a good idea, Dora.

Alec: Hey, Dora. What about that game?

Luca: Yeah, we want to play!

Dora: Papa, may I go and play?

Dora's Papa: Yes, that's fine.

Alec: Hooray!

Luca: Finally!

Alec: All of this talk about food is making me hungry.

Luca: I was thinking of stickball.
Now I'm thinking of meatballs!

Dora's Papa: That reminds me. Dora,
be back in time for dinner.

Dora: I will. Hey! We should all have dinner to welcome Camila's family to the neighborhood.

Alec: I'll bring pita bread!

Luca: I'll bring meatballs!

Camila: I'll bring plantains!

Dora's Papa: You see, Camila? In America, we say, "Welcome" with food!

All: The end.

Chapter 6

People and Money

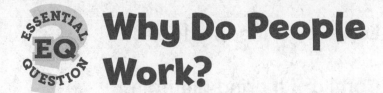

ESSENTIAL EQ QUESTION

Why Do People Work?

In this chapter, you'll learn why people work. You'll learn about trading and what it means to make money. You will also learn the difference between wants and needs. At the end of the chapter, you'll create a market in the classroom. In this classroom market, you will pretend to trade or purchase goods and services with your classmates.

Talk About It
COLLABORATE

Discuss with a partner what questions you have about why people work and the jobs they do.

My Research Questions

1._____

_____

2._____

_____

HSS 1.2.1, HSS 1.2.3, HSS 1.2.4, HSS 1.4.1,
HSS 1.4.3, HSS 1.6, HSS 1.6.1,
HSS 1.6.2, HAS.CS.1.2, HAS.CS.1.3,
HAS.CS.1.5, HAS.HR.1.1, HAS.HR.1.2,
HAS.HI.1.4

Inquiry Project

Classroom Market

In this project, you'll work as a class to create a classroom market for trading and purchasing goods and services.

Here's your project checklist.

☐ **Brainstorm** ideas for the classroom market. What kinds of goods and services do you want to be able to buy?

☐ **Choose** four goods and two services as a class. These will be the goods and services for sale in the market.

☐ **Talk** about rules for the market. What rules can you follow to be fair? What rules can you follow to get along?

☐ **Create** a sign for your good or service. This sign will show what you are selling.

☐ **Present** your sign to the class. Describe what you are selling. Answer any questions about your good or service.

Explore Words

Complete this chapter's Word Rater. Write notes as you learn more about each word.

factory

My Notes

☐ Know It!

☐ Heard It!

☐ Don't Know It!

_____

_____

_____

_____

needs

My Notes

☐ Know It!

☐ Heard It!

☐ Don't Know It!

_____

_____

_____

_____

trade

My Notes

☐ Know It!

☐ Heard It!

☐ Don't Know It!

_____

_____

_____

_____

volunteer   My Notes

☐ Know It!   _____

☐ Heard It!

☐ Don't Know It!   _____

          _____

wants   My Notes

☐ Know It!   _____

☐ Heard It!

☐ Don't Know It!   _____

          _____

Lesson Outcomes

What Am I Learning?

You will learn about goods and services.

Why Am I Learning It?

You will understand what people make and buy in your community.

How Will I Know that I Learned It?

You will show and explain the differences between goods and services.

Talk About It

Read the poem. What is one thing the poem tells you about goods? What is one thing the poem tells you about services?

Lifesize/Getty Images

Goods and Services

Goods are different things

That people make and use.

We can buy and sell

Any goods we choose.

Services are jobs or work

One person does for another.

We can buy or sell

Services to each other.

Goods and Services

1 Inspect

Look at the title. What do you think this chart will show?

Circle two pictures of goods.

Underline two pictures of services.

My Notes

_____

_____

_____

_____

_____

_____

Goods

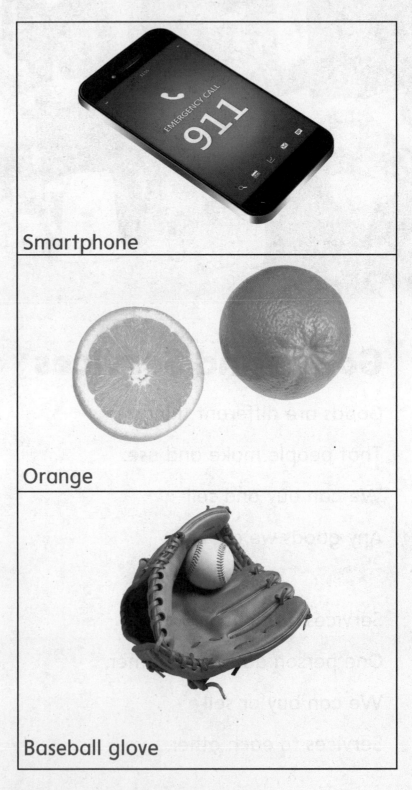

Smartphone

Orange

Baseball glove

Services

Dentist

Teacher

Server

2 Find Evidence

Reread Look at the chart. Who would help you in a restaurant?

3 Make Connections

Talk What goods do you use every day in school? What is an important service in your community?

COLLABORATE

Explore Key Details

Key details tell information about a main topic.

Use words and photos to help you find key details.

To find the key details:

1. Read the whole text.

2. Circle words that give bits of important information.

3. Look carefully at the photos. Look for helpful information.

COLLABORATE Work with your class to complete the graphic organizer.

Goods	Services
Apple	Mail carrier

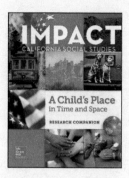

Investigate!

Read pages 248–253 in your Research Companion.

Look for text evidence that tells you the key details about goods and services.

Write your information in the graphic organizer.

Goods	Services
Definition: Objects you can _____.	Definition: Things that people _____.
Orange juice	Farmworker

Think About It

Think about what your research.
Why do we need goods and services?

Write About It

Define

What are goods and services?

Goods are _____

_____

Services are _____

_____

Write and Cite Evidence

Name one good. Name one service. Tell how they are
different.

_____

_____

_____

Talk About It

COLLABORATE

Tell your partner about your good and service.
Can he or she explain which is a good and which is
a service?

Civics

Connect to the ESSENTIAL EQ QUESTION

Take Action

What goods and services are important in your
community? Write an advertisement for one.
Tell whether it is for a good or a service.

_____

_____

_____

_____

_____

_____

How Do People Trade with Others?

Lesson Outcomes

What Am I Learning?

You will explore what trade is and how people trade with others.

Why Am I Learning It?

You will learn why and how people trade and why it is important.

How Will I Know that I Learned It?

You will show how you can earn and spend money.

Talk About It COLLABORATE

Look closely at the picture. What do you see? What are the children doing?

1 Inspect

Look at the title and the pictures. What do you think this text will be about?

Circle words you don't know.

Underline clues that tell you:

• what trade is.
• what money is.

My Notes

_____

_____

_____

_____

_____

Trade and Money

Have you ever traded something? Maybe you gave your friend a book. Then your friend gave you one of his or her books.

You **trade** when you give something to get something else. People trade to get what they want or need. One group of people might have a lot of food. Another group might have many tools. The groups can trade food and tools to get what they need.

Today most people use money to get things. Money is coins or paper bills. Money makes trading easy. People work to get money. They use money to buy goods.

People use money to buy things.

2 Find Evidence

Reread Why do people trade?

Underline the clues that help you answer.

3 Make Connections

Talk Turn back to page 269. Why are these children trading?

Explore Ask and Answer Questions

You can ask yourself questions about what you read.

This will help you think about the parts you do not understand.

Look in the text for answers to your questions.

COLLABORATE Work with your class to complete the graphic organizer.

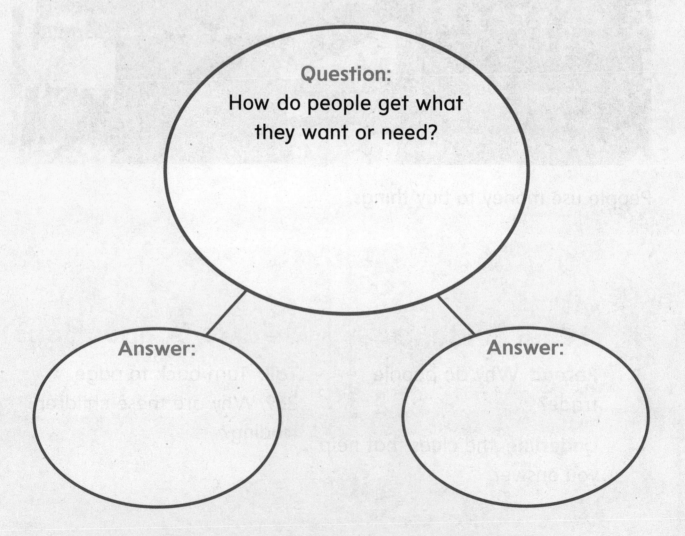

Question:
How do people get what they want or need?

Answer:

Answer:

Investigate!

Read pages 254–259 in your Research Companion.

Look for details about how goods get from one place to another.

Write your information in the graphic organizer.

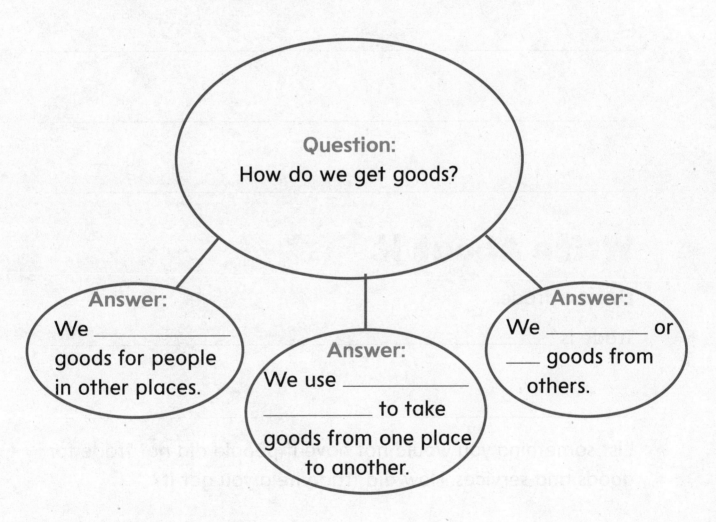

Question:
How do we get goods?

Answer:
We _____ goods for people in other places.

Answer:
We use _____ _____ to take goods from one place to another.

Answer:
We _____ or ____ goods from others.

Think About It

Think about what you learned. What does it mean to trade?

_____

_____

_____

Write About It

Define trade.

Trade is _____

_____.

List something you would not have if people did not trade for goods and services. How did trade help you get it?

_____

_____

Talk About It COLLABORATE

Share your writing with a partner. How does trade help you get goods and services?

_____

_____

Economics

Connect to the ESSENTIAL QUESTION EQ

Pretend you did a chore and earned money. Draw a picture of a good you would buy with the money you earned from working hard.

Lesson 3

What Kinds of Jobs Do People Do?

Lesson Outcomes

What Am I Learning?
You will learn what kinds of jobs people do.

Why Am I Learning It?
You will name places where people go to work and think about why we need these jobs.

How Will I Know that I Learned It?
You will write about different kinds of jobs.

Talk About It

Look at the picture.
Where do you think this person works?

What other work might this person do each day?

Jobs

1 Inspect

Read the title. What do you think this text will be about?

Circle words you don't know.

Underline clues that tell you:

- why people have jobs.
- what kinds of jobs people can do.

My Notes

_____

_____

_____

_____

Most people have jobs. This is how people get money. At a job, people trade work for money. People need money to get goods. They need money to use services. People pay for things they need.

There are many kinds of jobs. Workers do things that help others. An office worker may talk on the phone or work with computers. A factory worker makes things. A scientist works in a lab to discover new things.

Office workers use computers at their jobs.

Ariel Skelley/Getty Images

Crossing guards have the job of keeping children safe.

There are other kinds of jobs, too. Some people work as a police officer or a firefighter. When you are sick, you go to see a doctor.

Some people take care of places or animals. A park ranger takes care of a park. A zookeeper looks after animals. Those sound like fun jobs!

People make money at their jobs. They use money to buy things they want or need. Jobs are an important part of our world.

2 Find Evidence

Reread the text.

Underline the words that tell what people use their money for.

3 Make Connections

Talk What kinds of jobs do people do in your community?

COLLABORATE

Explore Fact and Opinion

A **fact** is a statement that is true all the time, no matter who is reading or saying it.

An **opinion** is what a person thinks or believes. Opinions can be different for different people.

COLLABORATE   As you read the text, work with your class to complete the graphic organizer.

Fact	Opinion
People need money to get goods.	Jobs are an important part of our world.

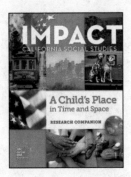

Investigate!

Read pages 260–267 in your Research Companion.

Look for details about the kinds of jobs that people do.

Write the details in your graphic organizer.

Fact	Opinion
Firefighters are always ready to protect people.	
	Volunteers are very important.
Jacob Lawrence was a painter.	

Think About It

Think about what you read. What kinds of jobs do people do?

Write About It

List three places where people can work.

1. _____

_____

_____

2. _____

_____

3. _____

_____

Talk About It

COLLABORATE

Discuss

Share your responses with your partner.
Talk about what jobs you think you would like to do.

Connect to the ESSENTIAL EQ QUESTION?

Civics

Why do people work? Choose
one job and list three reasons why someone would work at that job.

Job: _____

Reason # 1: _____

_____

Reason # 2: _____

_____

Reason # 3: _____

_____

Lesson 4 — How Are Wants and Needs Different?

Lesson Outcomes

What Am I Learning?
You will explore the difference between needs and wants.

Why Am I Learning It?
You will understand what things people need and how they are different from things people want.

How Will I Know that I Learned It?
You will write about making good choices between wants and needs.

Talk About It

Look at the picture. What do you think the children are doing? What details make you think so?

Look at the photos. What do you think is one answer to this question?

Underline key details in the text.

Circle words you don't know.

My Notes

_____

_____

_____

_____

_____

Why Do We Spend Money?

People need certain things to live. We need air, water, food, and clothes. We also need shelter. Shelter is a place to live. The things we need are necessary. That means we cannot live without them. Only air is free. The rest cost money.

We only have a certain amount of money. We have to make good choices about how we use our money. We should not use it to get only the things that we want. Then we may not have any left for the things we need.

Pretend you have some money to buy new shoes. But you decide to buy a toy and stickers first. Now you might not have enough money left for the shoes. Playing in shoes that no longer fit is no fun!

This girl wants a new bike.

2 Find Evidence

Reread the text.

Circle information that tells about the things you need and the things you want.

3 Make Connections

Talk How do we choose what to buy? What kinds of things might this dad and daughter need to think about before they decide to buy a bike?

Explore Classify

When you **classify**, you put things that are alike into groups.

COLLABORATE

As you read the text, work with your class to complete the graphic organizer.

Needs	Wants
Air	Toys

Investigate!

Read pages 268-273 in your Research Companion.

Look for details that help you classify needs and wants.

Write or draw your notes or pictures in this chart.

Needs	Wants
Shelter	Games

Think About It

Think about what you read.

What is the difference between needs and wants?

_____

_____

_____

Write About It

List one thing you need and one thing you want.

One thing I need is _____

_____

_____ .

One thing I want is _____

_____ .

Talk About It

COLLABORATE

Talk with your partner. What is a thing your partner needs? What is a thing your partner wants? How can you tell?

conomics

Connect to the

ESSENTIAL EQ QUESTION

Why do people have to make choices about money?

_____

_____

_____

_____

_____

_____

Inquiry Project Wrap Up

Classroom Market

Now's the time for your team to share your project. Here's what to do.

☐ Show the class your sign. Describe your good or service.

☐ You can say "I think you should buy our _____ because _____."

☐ Answer any questions your classmates might have.

☐ Open your store for business!

Tips for Presenting

Remember these tips when you present to your class.

☐ Hold up your sign so everyone can see.

☐ Speak loudly and clearly.

☐ Connect with your listeners.

☐ Remember to be a good citizen. Treat everyone with respect!

Project Rubric

Use these questions to help evaluate your project.

	Yes	No
Does our sign make people want to buy our good or service?		
Is our sign clear and easy to read? Does it have a big picture that makes people notice it?		
Did we describe the good or service with interesting details?		
Did we all work as a team?		
Did we treat others fairly and with respect?		

Project Reflection

Think about the work that you did in this chapter, either with a group or on your own. Describe something that you think you did very well. What would you do differently?

_____

_____

_____

Reference Sources

The Reference Section has a glossary of vocabulary words from the chapters in this book. Use this section to explore new vocabulary as you investigate and take action.

Glossary

A

address information that tells where a person lives

amendment an official change in the words or meaning of a law or document (such as a constitution)

B

border a line where one country or area ends and another begins

C

capital a city where the government of a country or state is located

celebrate to do something special or enjoyable for an important event, occasion, or holiday

citizen a person who lives in a particular place

colony an area that is controlled by or belongs to another country

community a group of people who live together in the same place

continent one of the seven large areas of land on Earth

culture the arts, beliefs, and customs of a particular group of people at a particular time

custom a way of acting that is usual among the people in a group

D

democracy a government that is run by the people who live under it

document an official paper that gives official information or proof about something

E

environment the natural world

equipment supplies or tools needed for a special purpose

F

factory a building or group of buildings where products are made

G

globe an object that is shaped like a large ball with a map of the world on it

government a group of people who control and make decisions for a country, state, city, or other place

H

history what happened in the past

holiday a special day to celebrate a person or event

I

immigrant a person who comes to a country in which he or she was not born

independence freedom from the control of another or others

interview a meeting to get information from someone; a report based on an interview

invent to make or think of something for the first time

invention something that is made for the first time

L

law a rule made by the government of a town, state, or country

location a place where something can be found

M

monument a building, statue, or other object made to honor a person or event

N

need something a person must have to live

neighborhood a small area in a town or city where people live

P

past a time that has gone by

produce to make something, especially by using machines

R

respect a feeling or understanding that someone or something is important and should be treated in an appropriate way

responsibility something a person should do

right something a person is free to do

S

symbol a picture that stands for something else

technology the use of science to invent useful things or to solve problems

trade the activity or process of buying, selling, or exchanging goods or services

tradition a custom that has been performed by the people in a particular group for a long time

transportation the act or process of moving people or things from one place to another

tribe a group of people who have the same language, customs, and beliefs

volunteer a person who works without pay to help other people

voting expressing a wish by making a choice that is counted

want something a person would like to have but does not need to live

Grade One
Historical and Social Sciences Content Standards and Analysis Skills

History-Social Science Content Standards.

A Child's Place in Time and Space

Students in grade one continue a more detailed treatment of the broad concepts of rights and responsibilities in the contemporary world. The classroom serves as a microcosm of society in which decisions are made with respect for individual responsibility, for other people, and for the rules by which we all must live: fair play, good sportsmanship, and respect for the rights and opinions of others. Students examine the geographic and economic aspects of life in their own neighborhoods and compare them to those of people long ago. Students explore the varied backgrounds of American citizens and learn about the symbols, icons, and songs that reflect our common heritage.

1.1 Students describe the rights and individual responsibilities of citizenship.
1. Understand the rule-making process in a direct democracy (everyone votes on the rules) and in a representative democracy (an elected group of people makes the rules), giving examples of both systems in their classroom, school, and community.
2. Understand the elements of fair play and good sportsmanship, respect for the rights and opinions of others, and respect for rules by which we live, including the meaning of the "Golden Rule."

1.2 Students compare and contrast the absolute and relative locations of places and people and describe the physical and/ or human characteristics of places.
1. Locate on maps and globes their local community, California, the United States, the seven continents, and the four oceans.
2. Compare the information that can be derived from a three-dimensional model to the information that can be derived from a picture of the same location.
3. Construct a simple map, using cardinal directions and map symbols.
4. Describe how location, weather, and physical environment affect the way people live, including the effects on their food, clothing, shelter, transportation, and recreation.

1.3 Students know and understand the symbols, icons, and traditions of the United States that provide continuity and a sense of community across time.
1. Recite the Pledge of Allegiance and sing songs that express American ideals (e.g., "America").
2. Understand the significance of our national holidays and the heroism and achievements of the people associated with them.
3. Identify American symbols, landmarks, and essential documents, such as the flag, bald eagle, Statue of Liberty, U.S. Constitution, and Declaration of Independence, and know the people and events associated with them.

1.4 Students compare and contrast everyday life in different times and places around the world and recognize that some aspects of people, places, and things change over time while others stay the same.
1. Examine the structure of schools and communities in the past.
2. Study transportation methods of earlier days.
3. Recognize similarities and differences of earlier generations in such areas as work (inside and outside the home), dress, manners, stories, games, and festivals, drawing from biographies, oral histories, and folklore.

I.5 Students describe the human characteristics of familiar places and the varied backgrounds of American citizens and residents in those places.

1. Recognize the ways in which they are all part of the same community, sharing principles, goals, and traditions despite their varied ancestry; the forms of diversity in their school and community; and the benefits and challenges of a diverse population.
2. Understand the ways in which American Indians and immigrants have helped define Californian and American culture.
3. Compare the beliefs, customs, ceremonies, traditions, and social practices of the varied cultures, drawing from folklore.

I. 6 Students understand basic economic concepts and the role of individual choice in a free-market economy.

1. Understand the concept of exchange and the use of money to purchase goods and services.
2. Identify the specialized work that people do to manufacture, transport, and market goods and services and the contributions of those who work in the home.

Historical and Social Sciences Analysis Skills

In addition to the standards, students demonstrate the following intellectual, reasoning, reflection, and research skills:

Chronological and Spatial Thinking

1. Students place key events and people of the historical era they are studying in a chronological sequence and within a spatial context; they interpret time lines.
2. Students correctly apply terms related to time, including *past, present, future, decade, century,* and *generation.*
3. Students explain how the present is connected to the past, identifying both similarities and differences between the two, and how some things change over time and some things stay the same.
4. Students use map and globe skills to determine the absolute locations of places and interpret information available through a map's or globe's legend, scale, and symbolic representations.
5. Students judge the significance of the relative location of a place (e.g., proximity to a harbor, on trade routes) and analyze how relative advantages or disadvantages can change over time.

Research, Evidence, and Point of View

1. Students differentiate between primary and secondary sources.
2. Students pose relevant questions about events they encounter in historical documents, eyewitness accounts, oral histories, letters, diaries, artifacts, photographs, maps, artworks, and architecture.
3. Students distinguish fact from fiction by comparing documentary sources on historical figures and events with fictionalized characters and events.

Historical Interpretation

1. Students summarize the key events of the era they are studying and explain the historical contexts of those events.
2. Students identify the human and physical characteristics of the places they are studying and explain how those features form the unique character of those places.
3. Students identify and interpret the multiple causes and effects of historical events.
4. Students conduct cost-benefit analyses of historical and current events.